My Patients With Tales

My Patients With Tales
The Experiences Of A Wisconsin Veterinarian

By Dr. Robert W. Pope

Published by: Pause Publishing Company
912 West Fourth Street
Mosinee, WI 54455

My Patients With Tales
(The Experiences Of A Wisconsin Veterinarian)

Scripture quotations are from the Authorized King James Version

Some names have been changed

Published by:
Pause Publishing Company
912 West Fourth Street
Mosinee, WI 54455
(715) 693-1699

Artwork by Marjorie Mae Pope

Photographs by Shel-Ray Studios
Bristol, WI

ISBN: 0-9669829-0-8
Library of Congress Catalog Card Number: 99-93073

Printed in the USA by
MP
Morris Publishing

This book is dedicated to:

my wife Marjorie
my daughters Sarah and Katie
(who encouraged me to tell these tales in written form)

my pets
Tova and Dasha — the dogs
Dorito, George, and Tuff — the cats
(who encourage me daily by bringing joy to my life)

Acknowledgments

I would like to acknowledge my clients who for the past twenty-five years have given me the opportunity to provide for the health care of their pets.

I would particularly like to acknowledge my patients, many are remembered even though only a few are recorded in these pages. For without animals, my tales would not be possible, and without them my life would be empty.

Table of Contents

chapter

1

A LIFE PRESERVER

Urgent was the message. A dog had drown. I watched as Paul placed Levi, his wife's West Highland White Terrier, on the table for me to examine. While I worked, Paul puffed nervously on his unlit pipe as if trying to draw air for the distressed dog. His wife, Linda, remained riveted in the doorway, unable to breathe freely.

Levi was family to them, Linda's child constant companion while Paul was away on business trips. Being 16 (a full dog lifetime for any canine), age was against Levi even before today's peril. And he had seen his share of veterinarians during those years, I being the last in a long line who tried to solve his canine conundrums.

Levi was hairless over most of his body due to a chronic skin allergy, but he never seemed to mind his naked state. Perhaps it was because his eyes, dulled and gray-white by old-age cataracts, couldn't see his hairlessness. Overall, his eyes seemed to match his dull sparse overcoat, giving him a gentlemanly demeanor, for a dog. His ears, one of his few furry regions, no longer twitched on alert, antenna-like and looking for sound. Then, he never was much of a watch dog. All that mattered to Levi was that his nose was true, and his legs were sound and able to carry him wherever he wanted to go. All that mattered to Paul and Linda was that Levi was all right.

Now this once hardy terrier appeared lifeless on my table, as his owners waited nervously for my evaluation. I pressed my stethoscope tightly against his chest. His heart pounded out irregular but strong beats. His mouth sucked up air and forced it down lower to the lungs, and they in turn squeezed the leftovers back out the nose. No water dammed up the path. His mucus membranes were porcelain white, a reflection of his shock-like state, but in his gray eyes I could see life.

He would recover, and I told them so. It was only then that I asked for the details I knew Paul would supply. "What happened?" I asked.

Paul removed the pipe from his mouth, and kept shifting his head from side to side. Linda finally exhaled and moved two steps into the exam room.

"We were on a pontoon boat with friends, "said Paul. "Linda had put Levi down, and I was telling them about the time Levi urinated on a friend's leg. Before I could finish the story, Levi walked right off the end of the boat as if he was a pirate walking the plank. I saw him flaying his legs back and forth trying to stay afloat, but I could see he was going down. So without hesitating, I leaped in after him, and grabbed the scruff of his neck just before he sank. Then I panicked, and started sinking with him. You know, I don't swim. My friend pulled us both out of the water."

"Levi stopped breathing – I thought he was dead," Paul continued, "so I shook him a few times, and then I gave him mouth-to-mouth. He gasped and choked, then he started breathing erratically. I called right away."

Even as I listened to this Bay Beach rescue, the life in Levi's eyes spread to his other organs. My stethoscope told me his breathing was becoming more regular as the demand for oxygen became satisfied, and his erratic heart settled down to a more methodical pace. Some color returned to his gums.

"He's doing better," I said. Then after administering some medicine to speed recovery, I gave Linda some nursing care instructions and sent the family home. Levi recovered.

Levi's next visit occurred when new hairless regions exploded with red craters from his constant battle with allergies. After my usual treatment that brought a temporary truce to his skin, I listened as Paul related more in his saga of life with Levi.

"I was real worried after Levi's drowning accident, so I bought an item mail-order to prevent another disaster when we go boating. It's a life-preserver-made-for-dogs. Linda thinks I'm crazy, and I spent too much for it. Extravagant she said. It may seem silly, but it fits him, and it covers up his baldness."

I laughed out loud at Paul, as much as with him, a personal flotation device for dogs. I thought he should have invested his time and money in swimming lessons for himself. But each time I saw Paul, he stressed his faithfulness in the buckle-up-for-safety campaign for Levi with his life-preserver-for-dogs. I envisioned Levi dressed in blaze orange like a lost deer hunter pacing on deck, or, perhaps, bobbing up and down in the blue water.

Then Paul told me about a recent change in his life "Maybe I'm having one of those mid-life things, but I quit my job this week, and I took a new job in town where I don't have to travel so much. Now I can be home almost every night. I've been married for 17 years, but only home for seven."

I understood, he was doing this for Linda, all of it – the job change, the end of overnight travels, and the life preserver for Levi.

But it wasn't until then that I fathomed the extent of his actions toward her balding 16 year old dog – his heroic water rescue when he couldn't swim, and his purchase of an overpriced personal flotation device. The love Paul embraced for his wife was so powerful that it drove him to love her dog.

Love, extravagant love, is like that, a life preserver.

Robert Pope

chapter
2

JUST LIKE A SHEEP

Think spring and well-adjusted Midwesterners will think about trilliums unfolding their leaves, the smell of fresh-cut grass, and the sound of baby birds. But spring to any veterinarian in mixed animal practice is about delivering calves in muddy fields, repairing dogs hit by automobiles, and a host of weather related sicknesses.

Spring for a veterinarian breeds an attitude problem, because it's a period to endure, not a season to enjoy.

This particular spring was saturated more than most with business. This particular day was Sunday, and I didn't want to be on-the-job with veterinary medicine. I wanted to be home with my family for a peaceful Sunday of God-given rest. This, of course, became the breeding ground for bad attitudes.

The telephone rang early that morning. A horse had been cut on a barbed wire fence, and was in need of sutures and a tetanus shot. That's when my attitude began its downward plunge. Horse work. I don't like horse work, because horses are flighty and unpredictable, making them dangerous to work on. Horses, in my part of the country, are the backyard variety. They get cut on barbed wire. The backyard variety also bolts at the sight of a stranger, and I was the worst kind of stranger to a horse.

Reluctantly, I put on my working clothes and attempted to suppress my negative thoughts. I rolled down the window of my truck, let the sun warm my face and the chilling spring breeze blow away a tiny hairbreadth of my irritability. Driving in the outdoors like this is what country veterinary practice was supposed to be about.

I attended to the horse's wounds, and gave my after-care instructions to the owner. I headed for home humming along with the soft music on the radio. The day had just begun and I still had time enjoy some Sunday rest. I was in a middle-mellow mood when the second call came.

"Go to the Bernard Dahm place for a sick sheep," the two way radio blared out. My humming stopped and my attitude slipped a notch closer toward crankiness – thinking more negative thoughts.

"Why didn't he call yesterday if it was that sick? He only has a few sheep, why did he have them anyway? What about the old adage, 'a sick sheep is a dead sheep '– it's probably already too late to do any good."

I tried hard to suppress these bad thoughts and concluded that if I picked up my working pace, I could still find time for rest. My mind was racing as I drove in the farm yard, slammed on the breaks, jumped out of my truck, and proclaimed in one breath, "Where's the sick sheep?"

The owner, an aging man with a pie plate face, was stuffed inside his olive green work overalls, which were stained brown from the knees down to his rubber boots. He smiled, and, being a man of few words said only, "She's out there."

Out there was a fenced in field of about two acres. Out there were nine or ten sheep. And out there among them was my patient. Even from where I watched, it wasn't hard to pick her out from among her clone-like allies and assess her problem. Her sides were heaving rapidly in and out like a blacksmith's bellows, feeding a dying flame. The chilling springtime air made her breath visible, and her open mouth breathing was obvious. She had pneumonia.

I remember thinking, "This isn't going to take too long. I'll take her temperature, I'll listen to her lungs, I'll give her an injection of antibiotics, and then I'm gone."

Gathering up my instruments and medicine, I marched out into the field with the owner trailing behind me.

As I approached my patient, she ran just past my reach to the other side of the fenced-in yard, her comrades close by her side. I walked slower the next time, a sneak-attack approach. But again she ran past me with the other sheep to the opposite area of the field. She was heaving and wheezing as she trotted by.

Now I was getting angry, and my frustration showed as I made one futile attempt after another to grab her. I tried picking up the pace. I should be able to out-run a sheep on death's doorstep, but I was beginning to wheeze a bit myself.

When she marched past me the next time, out of desperation, I lunged at her. I came away with a fist full of wool. The forward momentum threw me off balance, and I landed face-down on a ground lumpy with sheep mounds.

Lying there on the semi-frozen pasture in the mid-morning sun, face-and-nose eye-to-eye with sheep droppings, I began to laugh.

Mr. Dahm must have thought me a most unusual veterinarian. I came charging onto the scene, briskly attacking the problem and obviously irritated, then fall on my face and start to laugh.

I laughed because I was suddenly given a Sunday sermon. A sermon of circumstances especially orchestrated for my ears. A sermon of six short words . . ."Just like a sheep I am." Herd-oriented, parasite-prone, follow-the-leader, flighty-type-of- creature that sheep are, so am I.

"The Lord is my Shepherd . . ." and for that to be true, I must be like a sheep.

3

WHAT'S IN A NAME

"What's your puppy's name?" asked my receptionist.

"Her name is Cuddles," said the young mother. She navigated her baby in a stroller with one arm, and had a puppy tucked under the other.

"And what breed is she?"

"Oh, her mother was a Black Lab and her father a Saint Bernard – at least that's what the people said where I got her. How big do you think she'll get?"

As a veterinarian, I'm spellbound by the names people give their animals. A story unfolds from every pet I put to the question, "What's in that name?" Man's best friend can be called in numerous ways. My own dog is a playful Siberian Husky. I call him Tova – short for Tovarich – which in Russian means, good friend.

Some names come in a colorful array: Buffy, the sturdy Cocker Spaniel; Blackie, the strong and athletic Labrador Retriever; Rusty, the gentle Golden Retriever; and Red, the aristocratic Irish Setter.

Other names portray the popular "hero" of the times: Morris the cat, Colonel North the German Shepherd (affectionately called Colonel), and Gizmo the noble Shih Tzu.

Sometimes a name can bring a mental image to mind even before the first visit. I remember the day Rambo popped up on the appointment book for vaccinations. I anticipated an encounter with an aggressive opponent, but when I entered the examination room, I got my first glimpse of Rambo. He tipped the scales at five pounds and turned out to be a timid Sheltie puppy.

Compounding things are twin pets, with twin names. My favorites are the chocolate colored part-Burmese cats named Snickers and Hershey, or the two miniature black poodles named Buttons and Bows. Cupcake and Devil's Food are two kittens born to Marblecake, a calico angel.

Some names just never seem to measure up. The 120 pound Black Lab/Irish Setter named Teddy is one. His full and proper name is Teddy Bear, and at one time I'm sure he was one, but now he's just The Bear.

Mysteries abound in the initials some owners give their pets as names. J.D. was Jesse's dog, and T.C. is short for Tom Cat. And the kitten named A.D. tops them all. She was a small, half-starved half-frozen kitten found along the busy interstate expressway – Almost Dead.

Other pets are named for their habits: Rocky, the English Setter who eats rocks; Dorito, the short haired tabby cat who eats chips fallen to the floor; and Wags, the little Lhasa who's stubby tail never stops.

The most unusual name I encountered belonged to an ordinary orange tabby cat named Pickles. She began life as Phil, but close investigation revealed the he was not a he, so keeping true to form, Phil became Phyllis. This, however, reminded the owner of Phyllis Diller, which in turn reminder her of dill pickles – a
perfect name.

The most unimaginative names are given to hunting dogs. I'm never impressed by the long line of Beagles with names like Buck, Duke, Jake, or Joe. Coon dogs often have such hackneyed names as Blue, Beau, or Doc. These hard-working, useful friends should have more noble names.

Recently, I discovered the reason for these monosyllabic titles. During hunting, a loud call of one syllable can be heard to the farthest reaches of forest depths or creek bottom. The dog responds to the sound he hears and understands – a simple name.

When I think of names, I'm reminded of the many names God gives us for Himself. The list seems almost endless: Jehovah, King of Kings, Lord or lords, the Great Shepherd, God Almighty, Our Protector, Our Shield, Immanuel, the Alpha and the Omega. Each name gives new insight into the nature of God.

But one name, above all names, compels me to halt in awe. A simple name, but one I hear and understand. When Moses saw the burning bush and asked God, "Who shall I say has sent me?" God responded, ". . . Say to the sons of Israel, 'I AM' has sent me to you" (Ex.3:14) – a simple name.

chapter

4

ANIMAL DOCTOR

Margie and I had been married three and a half years, and I wore my wedding ring faithfully everyday since the first. And why shouldn't I? It was symbol of my marriage, and it was special because she made it in art class.

I had a new job, my first real job; finally I was a veterinarian. I was also a husband, a provider, and a going-to-be first time father.

I'd been working for several months learning my job, and the new skills were coming quickly. I was called out for many cows with calving complications, and I was getting good at manipulating twisted legs and tucked-under heads to deliver newborn calves. My long slim arms and six-foot plus frame pitched in a real advantage. I even fancied myself growing muscular from the work, maybe.

Late one summer evening, I answered a call from an anxious dairy farmer.

"I have a cow that can't have her calf," the dairy man said.

"What seems to be the problem?" I asked.

"Don't know for sure, maybe she's not ready, maybe she is, can't tell, but I can tell you better check her out tonight."

"I'll be there as soon as I can."

I arrived and filled my stainless steel pail with hot water from the milk house. Then I stripped to the waist, lubricated my arms liberally with disinfectant soap, and began working my hand and arm through the birth canal trying to feel a head or feet or legs.

As I entered the cow's reproductive tract, my arm kept twisting in one direction. This was strange, I hadn't felt anything like that before. I guided my hand carefully farther and farther inside the cow, until finally the uterus expanded to where I could feel the calf's head at the tip of my finger. I felt its nose and legs.

In the process of manipulations and contortions my wedding ring slipped off my finger and disappeared into the depths of the cow's boundless uterus.

Sorting out the parts of the calf was soon forgotten as I frantically fished for the ring.

* * * * * * * *

How did I get to this point in my life? How did a Chicago suburban-raised son of a dentist end up as a veterinarian on rural dairy farm with his arm inside a cow?

It began in my childhood when animals were part of my life, but not in a positive way.

When I was five my father bought a dog from the Sears and Roebuck catalog – a cream colored Cocker Spaniel we named Rex. He became a dominant dog with biting tendencies. One day he bit me severely when I was playing with him, and some time later he bit a neighborhood boy when he ran through our back yard. My father found him another home and said we were better off dog-less.

It was years before the family would try another dog. I was in sixth grade this time, and we choose a black-and-tan Dachshund from a pet store. We named him Prince.

I became the designated pooper-picker-upper when he spread his good tidings around the utility room floor. Prince hated to be left alone, so we locked him in the small furnace room which was also the home of two guinea pigs named Queenie and Toeinquo. He must have hated the furry rodents too, because when given the chance, he assassinated them both.

Prince hated going to the kennel, he hated the mailman, but most of all he hated the veterinarian. Our entire family was so fearful of the experience that Prince rarely received veterinary care, and never received his vaccinations. In spite of this he lived to the prime age of 15.

We had other pets, but it was my sister who loved animals. In addition to the guinea pigs, she had a beautiful grey smoke Persian cat named Lucky Lady. She was a neurotic feline with a personality disorder who only liked my sister, and then only sometimes.

My sister also acquired a horse named Maverick. He was an overgrown half-quarter half-Morgan beast of an animal with a mouth too big for a bit. My sister had no saddle to straddle him, so she never mustered up the courage for a ride.

While growing up my interests were not in animals but in Boy Scouts. It was here, in the rigors of scouting, that my father poured

24

out his energy for his sons. We did scouting right. We camped, we went to all the special meetings, Jamborees, and Boy Scout experiences.

My goal was to become an Eagle Scout. This was no small task, because it took many years of hard work up the ranks from Tenderfoot to Second Class, then First Class, Star, Life, and finally Eagle Scout.

To me, becoming an Eagle Scout was better than being nominated school crossing guard of the year. Stories were told of grey haired winos that were Eagle Scouts. These down-and-outers could flash their faded Eagle Scout card to obtain instant success in a glamorous job any time they wanted, all because they were Eagle Scouts.

Merit badges were the ticket to becoming an Eagle Scout, and they were hard to obtain. A scout had to earn a merit badge. It often took months of effort to complete the requirements for just one badge. After all the work, a scout still had one ordeal – to pass an examination with the merit badge counselor.

I still remember one merit badge counselor in particular. He was a tall, statuary, sullen man with a deep voice. My father drove me to his house and left me there at the front door by myself. I felt like a sale barn calf led to slaughter.

Once inside I was ushered to an over-fluffed sofa in the living room of this strange man's house – a house that smelled of pine air fresheners and furniture polish. My stomach did cartwheels from a combination of nervousness and odors.

Merit badge counselors grilled me extensively on what I had learned. First Aid merit badge – "Describe the causes and signs of shock. Explain what should be done for severe bleeding." Public Health merit badge – "Explain the difference between an infectious disease and a chronic disease. Name two diseases against which you, at Scout age, should be immunized." Safety merit badge – "Describe safety practices in the home that help prevent falls, burns and scalds and poisonings."

Merit badges were hard work.

Summertime was the best time to work on merit badges, and summer camp was the best place. In two weeks a scout could earn three, maybe more merit badges. Daily lessons were given in life saving, swimming, canoeing and other necessary badges. One summer, I spent hours in the nature department working on Bird

Study, Nature, and Animal Industry merit badges. I learned all the breeds of cattle and sheep that summer, but most of all I learned to love the outdoors. I wanted to stay at camp all year.

One weekend an event happened that would eventually change my life. A special merit badge opportunity was given to our Northwest Suburban Troop 155. This was to be a unique weekend camp out to earn merit badges. A whole summer rolled up into one weekend. I needed more merit badges to complete my Eagle Scout, and especially canoeing – hard for a kid from the Chicago Suburbs. Here was my opportunity.

On a Saturday morning at Illinois State Beach Park on Lake Michigan, fighting strong winds and tall waves, I earned my canoeing merit badge.

During lunch a fellow scout told me about how easily he passed the First Aid to Animals merit badge. The counselor was a marshmallow who only asked a couple of simple questions. He coaxed me to try for the badge that afternoon.

I read the requirements, which didn't seem too difficult. "Present evidence that you have assisted in the care of an injured or sick animal for a period of at least four days." Prince, the dog that hated vets, was the perfect project – he was sick all the time, wasn't he? I stretched the facts to fit the merit badge requirements.

I returned in fifteen minutes. I had passed First Aid To Animals merit badge, but a bit too easily.

I finally received all 21 badges necessary for my Eagle Scout rank. My goal had been achieved. I received my Eagle Scout rank on September 25, 1963.

College followed.

I entered a pre-medical program at the University of Wisconsin at Madison. It was my Father's dream and goal for me. My energy was siphoned into my course of study with the same enthusiasm that I had for merit badges.

I worked through all the required courses: physics, chemistry, biology, more chemistry, genetics. I enjoyed the outdoor classes most: ornithology, botany, plant geography, and wildlife ecology – even though they weren't important for doctors.

Three years passed quickly and the time approached for my application to medical schools. That meant I had to take the well known and hated MCAT exam (Medical College Admission Test).

One Saturday morning I squeezed into a classroom with a football stadium sized crowd to take the test. I looked from face to face and saw serious determination everywhere. All categories of people were present: tall and short ones, black and white, female, male. All came with a dream and desire to become a physician. I took the exam, but for the first time I was confused about what I wanted to do with my life.

Was medicine really for me? Did I want to be stuffed inside a hospital for the rest of my life? Wouldn't I rather be outside working where I enjoyed things? These question passed through my mind multiple times in the weeks after the exam.

It was Margie, my wife-to-be, that gave direction to my confusion.

At the time I was taking a class in botany and I needed to collect 50 different flowering plant species before the end of the semester. The problem was that it was already late fall and most plants had prepared for winter leaving only dry stalks instead of flowers.

I spent several weekends at Margie's parents' rural Wisconsin dairy farm collecting plants. One night a cow was sick, and they called the veterinarian. Watching him treat the comatose cow and seeing her almost jump-started to new life gave me a new dream. Veterinary medicine would combine my medical interest and desire to be outdoors.

Shortly thereafter I applied to veterinary school. I started classes in the fall of 1970.

Margie and I were married on December 26, 1970. I spent the next four years in serious studies. Margie worked as an art teacher in a rural town 30 miles away. My summers were spent working for tuition and learning all I could.

I graduated from veterinary school in June of 1974 and took a position in the town of Plain, Wisconsin, population 690 ½. That's if you counted me, my wife, and our baby which was due 4 months.

* * * * * * * *

Now I was here, my arm inside a cow, my wedding ring lost. What now?

Not wanting to show my concern to the dairyman nor my ignorance of this peculiar uterus, I said nothing. The farmer also remained stoically quiet while I worked. But all this time I was looking for the ring and thinking about my past, he thought I was working on the calf.

I trolled around inside the cow's uterus, back and forth for several minutes until I finally snagged the ring. Then I casually slipped the ring safely into my deepest pocket.

I told the owner with all the confidence a novice could muster up, "I'll be back in the morning, she's not opened up enough to have this calf.

That night, I had time to think about the problem, and realized that the cow's trouble was a twisted or flipped uterus. This condition had not allowed the cervix to dilate. Called a uterine torsion, this calving difficulty plagued me frequently during the next 10 years of dairy practice.

That night I also thought about myself and I realized that I had earned my First Aid to Animals Merit Badge.

In the morning I left the house for the first time without wearing my wedding ring. But I knew where I was going, and I knew what was important.

I returned to the farm and delivered a live, healthy calf.

chapter

5

THE MOVE NORTH

Word had spread around the farming community even though it was a late lazy Sunday summer. I glanced over my shoulder at the stack of hay bales in the empty cow stanchion. Pairs of eyes stared at me as I prepared for surgery. A congregation of onlookers had gathered like a flock of curious geese to watch my bovine operation. My patient, a veteran in the calving business could not deliver her calf, and neither could I, at least not without my scalpel. My audience, which consisted of several young people and adults who had never witnessed cow surgery, came to see the doctor take the calf "out the side of the cow."

I didn't mind, because for me, it became an opportunity to teach, and a few extra hands were always welcome. I rarely had enough help for on the farm surgeries.

Although I was new to North-central Wisconsin, I was a seasoned professional to the cow community. I came from Southwest Wisconsin with ten full months of experience in bovine medicine and surgery. In that time I had preformed several C-section surgeries.

I brought my family with me for the day because it was the only time in weeks they had seen me. Margie carried our 7 month old daughter, Sarah, and a supply of ready made bottles of special infant formula. Sarah was drinking only special formula, because she vomited violently after drinking regular store-bought cow's milk. The pediatrician thought it was because she was born several weeks premature.

But Sarah had finished her last bottle several hours earlier, and four farm visits ago (one more than normal). Now she was hungry and crying. My family was inside the farm house kitchen, and I was out in the barn with an audience.

I began the long incision necessary for removing the calf. I started high in the flank just below the vertebra, and I kept my cut between the last rib and the back leg. This area was usually indented, but in

31

my patient it was budged out, all the spare room taken up by the large calf inside.

I pressed hard with my scalpel so I could penetrate the thick tough skin with one clean stroke. The skin separated, leaving exposed the white connective tissue with the pink muscle underneath. A few skin bleeders squirted red blood across my glasses. My audience moved further behind the hay bales for protection. I grabbed some gauze pads and a hemostat to control the damage. Gentle pressure for a minute or two, and then I would continue.

* * * * * * * *

I thought about our recent move.

I didn't want the move. I loved the hills and valleys of southwestern Wisconsin and the farms that occupied them. Sarah had been born there, and so had my career as a veterinarian. But the fickle, ever downward-sliding dairy economy had caused my employer to terminate my contract. I was forced to look elsewhere for work and a position.

I considered my own business, and seriously looked for a place, but the timing was not right. I needed another position to solidify my skills and become more financially secure.

Now I was here in this hill-less tree beset landscape known as the Dairy Capitol of the World. The county even had a sign to broadcast the fact: "Marathon County home of 186,000 Dairy Queens."

The practice certainly treated cows as royalty. But it took many hours of driving from farm to farm to treat the problems and find the farms carved out of the wooded countryside.

My day started early in the Northwoods, with the rising of the first dairyman sometimes before 5am, and it lasted until the last dairy queen was bedded down for the night often after the late night news. I rarely saw our daughter, and I was too tired to say but a few words to my wife. That's what made this Sunday with them special, even though I was in the barn doing cow surgery.

* * * * * * * *

The bleeding now stopped, and I returned to my work. I

extended my incision a few inches to allow room for the uterus, and then I cut through several muscle layers. I located the uterus and made an incision large enough to insert my hand. I located a back leg and pulled it outside the cow. My audience leaned over the hay bales for a closer look.

After extending the cut in the uterus further, I located the other back leg and removed a large healthy heifer calf. The farmer would be pleased. I turned around to find him, but he was absent from the crowd of onlookers.

"It's a heifer, Leonard!" I shouted.

"Good," he shouted back from the milk house. "I'm taking some fresh milk from the bulk tank up to the house. Your daughter is balling like that new born heifer."

"She can't handle cow's milk, Leonard, she gets sick on it," I said.

But he was gone before my protest reached his ears.

I turned back to my work in time to watch the calf shake her head several times and then snort out a spray of amniotic fluid. She tried several uncoordinated leg movements in an attempt to get up on her feet. Failing, she balled loudly once and remained sprawled out on the barn floor. The cow turned her head to look at her calf.

I began putting together the layers of the cow's uterus and muscle I had taken apart. Suturing always takes longer than slicing. My audience, one by one, drifted away. The excitement was over and interest in the cow (with the hole in her side) faded with each suture I placed. By the time I put in the last suture, I was alone.

I cleaned up in the milk house, and put my instruments away. Finished, I went back to the barn one last time to observe my patient. The cow looked me in the eyes for a moment, then gently nudged her calf who was now standing and getting her first meal. I accepted the gesture as a cow thank you and nodded back my approval. I walked slowly the farmhouse kitchen.

There I saw Margie feeding Sarah from a full bottle. She was content as a new born calf – her first meal of farm fresh cow's milk.

"How's the calf?" asked Margie.

"Just fine," I said. "How's Sarah?"

"Just fine."

6

FORTY ACRES OF CONCRETE

"Turn north on Glen Road off County C, the farm at the end of the road," she said.

The thirty-five mile drive gave me time to reflect my recent move to North Central Wisconsin. The Glenn's must be important or influential for a road named after them.

I turned north and found a wide gravel lane that took me to the farm. There, chiseled out of the dense pine forest, was a two-story white house, matching barn, and 80 acres of cleared land.

I carried my stainless pail to the milk house and found the hot water. Utensils from the morning milking were already clean and hanging on designated pegs. I walked halfway down the alley behind the cows and set my pail down.

I found Mr. Mike Glen, and introduced myself by shaking his big hands. His fingers and palm were marked with deep cracks stained white from barn lime. His glasses, speckled with brown, partly hid his soft blue eyes. He stood taller than my six feet with broader shoulders. He had snow white hair.

Smiling when he saw me, he said, "Jus' finished cleanin' d' barn."

I was to hear his local accent frequently during the next ten years. His father immigrated from Europe and cleared the land. Mike was home grown and never had a chance for much schooling, but he possessed a north-woods wisdom that comes from the cows, the land, and the weather, not from books or professors. He and his wife were wed to the cows and the land, and the bond was strong because neither had traveled more than 30 miles from the home farm.

We talked small talk while I treated his cow for mastitis.

"You should move near here," he said. "We need good young doctor like you for our cows."

A nine month gestation period passed, after which I found a house to rent which became home, and an abandoned barber shop, which became the Mosinee Veterinary Clinic. Mike Glen was the first to know.

I saw Mike Glen and his wife often throughout the years for cow ailments. They always worked side by side.

During these years of long hours and days without end, somehow I raised a family of two girls and grew a veterinary business.

One day I took my youngest daughter, Katie, now four years old, with me to the Glen's farm to treat a cow. Mrs. Glen took her by the hand and lead her to the house.

"I think I got a cookie for you," she said.

Katie returned with a small bag of candy and a big smile.

During another visit to the Glen's they had big news for me.

"I won trip for two to Oprey Land in Nashville," said Mrs. Glen. "From the radio station contest."

"My whole life, I never been anywhere," said Mike. "You'll come if cows are sick when we're gone?"

I reassured him that all would be well when he left, and wished them both a good time.

After they returned, I heard all about the trip.

"You should go there," Mike said. "They have a place for parking cars, forty acres of concrete. You can wear your white Sunday shoes all day and not get dirty. Forty acres of concrete!"

I smiled at the childlike wisdom of his experience, but it wasn't until several years later that his small-view of the world and experience hit me.

During another visit, I Told Mike I was going to a veterinary meeting in Las Vegas. "Don't get any sick cows while I'm gone," I said.

"Don't worry. You have good time. I've been there. They have forty acres of concrete to park cars, you can walk all day and not get your Sunday shoes dirty. Go, don't worry."

In Mike's experience, anywhere outside the county was were he had been on that one trip to Nashville. It wasn't his geography that was bad, but his experience was barren.

On our next family vacation, I took my daughters to Minneapolis, to broaden their experience of the world. I sought out the highest building I could find.

"Look out there, girls, see how big a place this is? There's more than forty acres of concrete out there."

36

"Dad, I'm going to write about this for school," said Sarah, my oldest daughter.

"Dad, what's an acre?" asked Katie.

It's been fifteen years since that conversation. Now both daughters are grown and have visited countries I only experience from books – Korea, Honduras, Slovakia.

When Katie returned from Korea recently, I asked her if they have many dogs and cats.

"No, Dad," she said, "they don't have pets. It's all concrete and high-rises in Seoul. Just acres and acres of concrete."

chapter
7

THE WILBER WHINER STORY

Puppy love is universal. Who doesn't love to hug one? But raising up a litter of puppies takes dedication. Many people do it, but few have the fortitude. Usually by the time those puppies are four weeks old, the joy is gone and they can't wait until the puppies are gone. Occasionally someone comes along who never seems to have enough of puppies. I call them puppy mothers. Janet was such a person.

Tasha Jo Lynn was Janet's companion, and a beautiful dog. Her blue eyes and dark face mask gave her the typical Siberian Husky look, but it was her gentle friendly temperament that made her Janet's friend and set her apart from the crowd.

Breeding Tasha was a planned event. The sire, Keno, owned by Janet's son, was a sharp featured red and white Husky with a noble aloofness and the harness power of two sled dogs. He was not at all like Tasha. I wondered which parent the puppies would take after.

Despite some minor problems, Tasha thrived throughout her pregnancy, and whelping went uneventfully. I examined five puppies soon after birth and declared them a healthy and priceless litter.

Janet named each puppy based on its characteristics: Bruiser, the biggest and first born; Minnie, the smallest and only female; Streak, the one with a white stripe down his dark face; Sleepy, the lazy fellow who ate sprawled out with his front paws hugging the food dish; and Wilber Whiner, the complainer.

Wilber was a whiner from birth. He would howl a little puppy howl, and whine pitifully whenever things didn't go his way. Then Janet would pick him up, give him a hug and talk softly to reassure him things were okay. This only a two legged mother could do.

I saw all of this in action during Wilber's first vaccination visit at six weeks of age. While still inside the cardboard box, he howled out his displeasure with the method of transportation and the clinical surroundings. Janet just hugged him.

The puppies grew, and I didn't see them again until they were nine weeks old, time for their booster vaccination. Janet was worried, because Streak had developed a problem, a sudden assault of vomiting followed by explosive diarrhea. After a thorough examination I, too, became concerned.

I suspected and then confirmed a disease called Parvovirus, a nasty infection that infiltrates the entire intestinal tract – mouth to tail. Parvo's severity shreds the intestinal lining like a paper cutter does paper. Often weakened puppies die. Somehow Parvovirus had broken through the vaccination defense walls.

I treated Streak, and he improved as suddenly as he became sick. But I was only cautiously optimistic, knowing the highly contagious nature of this disease. Every puppy was a breath away from this often fatal virus. I gave Janet a list of early warning signs of Parvo's arrival, and hoped we had seen the end of it.

Two days later Sleepy began the explosive vomiting which signaled the start of the virus. His symptoms were more severe than Streak's, but with treatment he recovered, only slower. The disease was picking up momentum with an increased virulence. Who would it strike next?

"Bruiser and Minnie were sold before the virus struck, so maybe they are safe," I told Janet. However, the tension remained so great that Janet, being a puppy mother, called Minnie and Bruiser's new owners daily for health updates. They remained symptomless

That left Wilber.

On the day Wilber Whiner became sick, everybody knew it. I examined him between whines, and since his condition was serious, I ordered an extended hospital stay in spite of his protests.

I treated Wilber with pills, injections, and liquids. Hoses hung at strategic locations from his body. I treated him one day then two, three, then four days. He withered weaker with each treatment. But even in this condition, he whined when he saw me, and complained continuously about hospital life.

Finally on day seven, he passed what I thought the critical plane, and his shaky condition stabilized. I knew he felt better because his whining increased several decibels. I sent him home that afternoon confident that familiar surroundings would be the missing medicine in his treatment. Besides, the whining was wearing me thin.

Home for less than a day, and Wilber was back to see me. He could not keep down even the simple baby food I had prescribed. His stomach, raw on the inside from damage I could not see, continued to refuse the blandest of diets.

40

Another hospital stay for Wilber was prescribed, with more medicine and more treatments and more whining – a full second week

This time he fought the intravenous feedings his body needed so desperately, and he whined relentlessly unless someone held him to be quiet. Everyone took turns holding him; members of my staff and my wife; but the largest burden fell on my daughters. They applied the big time required for Wilber's special care, and they talked to him with soothing words like Janet did when he whined.

Hugs calmed his whimpers, but stop for an instant, and he would fidget. Then in an eye's flash he could squirm loose from the tube that supplied his only strength. I would have to reinsert the tube and begin again. He did this several times even in his weakened condition.

Slowly Wilber's condition improved.

On day fourteen I was treating Wilber myself, holding him tight so he wouldn't cry. I needed some medication behind me, so I let him loose just for instant. Still, I kept one hand touching his head while I stretched for the medicine with the other. When I turned back, I discovered the intravenous tube and the needle on the floor, spitting out drops of physiological saline like a fire hose gone wild. Wilber just grinned at me. How he pulled off this magician's trick, I never found out.

I sent him home that afternoon.

At home this time, Wilber improved, although at a snail's pace. His emaciated body advertised every rib, and his large head to body ratio gave him a wolf-starved look. He weighed only 17 pounds when I sent him home. Sleepy topped the scale at a robust 38.

All this, the weight loss, the pathetic looks, the slow recovery, took nothing away from Wilber's characteristic voice-box whining.

Janet brought him in frequently for short check-ups. She brought Sleepy too, hoping to ease Wilber's fears. He grew to love my girls, and would go willingly to them for hugs and treats, returning kisses for their kindness. From me he kept his distance. Each visit evoked a howl stating firmly Wilber's position on the clinic environment. Even when I offered him special treats he was skeptical of my intentions, and watched me close for signs of needles or medicine.

One day Janet came to the clinic without Wilber. At first I thought something had happened to Wilber. Then I thought, maybe, Janet sold him. But she reassured me he was fine and at home.

"I don't think anyone will buy a dog named Wilber Whiner," she said. "So I changed his name to Wilbee."

"Why Wilbee?" I asked.

"Well, It's short for Will-Be-Good!"

And so, sometimes he is good. But sometimes, still, he's Wilber Whiner. I know because Janet never sold him. Now he is 80 pounds and strikingly beautiful like his mother, Tasha; and he possesses the harness power of a three dog sled team. Still, he stiffens with resistance when Janet drags him down the hallway to the exam room, and he whines at me and the cold stainless steel exam table. The same whine as the very first day. Janet just gives him a hug and talks softly to him, and then he's fine.

Now every time I get a puppy that whines, I remember Wilber and Janet. I give that puppy a little hug with a few softly spoken words. The whines soon fade to whimpers and the whimpers soon cease. Things are not so bad.

It works so well, I'm wondering if it works for people, too.

chapter
8

THE PYTHON

"Some guy on the phone wants to know if you treat snakes," said Joyce, my receptionist. Then she looked at the telephone cord that had coiled around her arm and dropped the receiver.

Until that call, I had never considered snakes as part of my responsibility. In all my years as a veterinarian (12 at the time), the subject never came up. Now I had to have an answer.

I had treated unusual animals before. Once I examined a bear cub for a traveling circus. That was unusual. And another time I was called to look at some pigmy goats that were the size of a beagle dog. All these had legs, four legs. Now I had been asked to exam a creature without appendages and who covered itself with scales instead of hair.

At least I could talk with the owner, and even if I had to examine his snake, I didn't have to become intimate with it. What type of person kept a snake as a pet? I thought all these things before acting. I know my curiosity caused me to pick up the telephone that now dangled from the wall like a vine from a tree in the tropical rainforest of Brazil.

"What's the problem with the snake?" I asked.

"He has three large lumps on his body. I think it's cancer."

The voice was that of a young man, and it had the ring of an owner with true concern for his animal. I decided I would help him the best I could. I began the way I always begin, by asking questions. Questions give me clues to the problem. Questions give me time to think about the possible solutions and the best course of action. The trouble here was that I didn't know the first thing about snakes, and I didn't know what questions to ask. I didn't know, so instead I asked the first thing that entered my mind.

"What kind of snake do you have?" My concern was big and poisonous.

"I've called several other veterinary clinics, and nobody else would even talk to me," said the owner, "Would you, please, look at him for me?"

Robert Pope

"What kind of snake is this?" I asked again. He gave no answer to my question the first time, so it must be poisonous and big.

"Oh, he's harmless, honest, and I can control him."

Harmless he said, so it's not poisonous. And he can control him, so it's not that big. Then I answered his question without receiving an answer to mine.

"I'll look at him for you, but what kind of snake is it?"

"He's a Reticulated Python, male, 13 feet in length, weighed 30 pounds last time I weighed him, small for the species, actually. I feed him once a month, and I fed him about a month ago."

Suddenly all the answers to all the questions I hadn't asked, but needed answers to, were spit out. And it's a good thing, because all I could focus my mind on was 13 feet, 30 pounds. At 30 pounds he weighed 10 pounds more than the beagle dog I had just vaccinated, and he was twice as long as me with a foot to spare. This was a big snake, a constrictor snake, a snake that kills his food by squeezing it to death. He said it hadn't eaten in a month. I thought about it, I would be very hungry in a month. Not poisonous, but certainly not harmless, either.

I told my staff about the upcoming visit. First they laughed at me. I wasn't serious. Then they pledged to me their unanimous absence from the scene. For this one I was on my own.

At the appointed date and time the snake owner arrived. His blond hair and brown eyes blended naturally with his well-worn blue jeans and tan plaid shirt. He looked normal, but I don't know what I expected, maybe circus attire of some kind. He greeted me with a nod of his head.

He carried in his arms an ordinary ten gallon glass aquarium with a lid. I couldn't see much through the glass, but I remember thinking, "this can't be big, it's only a fish tank."

After setting the tank down, he reached inside and removed the snake from his temporary travel home. He grabbed the head first, and then uncoiled it's powerful body. The python, fully extended, covered the entire length of my exam table and draped down the other side. I remained planted at the tail end. I kept chanting to myself, "pythons are constrictors, pythons are not poisonous, pythons are constrictors, pythons are not poisonous." It seemed to help. I hoped the owner knew what he was doing, because I didn't.

After the initial shock wore off, I began to focus on the problem. I could see the lumps rising from the spine of the snake in three

46

places. I searched my memory for facts about reptiles from my veterinary training. Not much there, that I remembered. Exotic medicine, then, had been a one week course in four long years of study.

While the owner gently stroked the head of his cold blooded friend, I examined the large lumps. At first I could only look at them from a distance. They rose abruptly from the body and shot upwards like mountain peaks from a level plain. I moved my eyes in closer for a detailed look, but I became distracted by the beautiful patterns of color made possible by the detailed design on each scale. Then I reached out to touch the lumps by running my hands along the snake's body. I expected a sandpaper feel, but I was surprised. The scales felt smooth and cool, so different than the bushy warm fur of my patients with legs. I repeated the procedure several times just for the experience.

Even though these sensations were new, the lumps felt familiar. They were firm to touch, but also spongy to feel, not like the hard tissue of cancer. I had felt masses like these on dogs and cats. They had the consistency of abscesses or boils. Snakes could get boils, I was sure of that fact, but how I didn't know. Cats usually got them from fighting with other cats, and dogs got them from puncture wounds.

I assured the owner the lumps were not cancerous, but rather large infections that required treatment. I outlined my plan (the same as for dogs or cats): first open up the abscess, second drain out the contents, and third, administer antibiotics.

I proceeded through the minor surgical procedure of opening and draining. My patient seemed content with the gentle and continual stroking of his head provided by his master. The entire procedure was actually easier to perform than on a dog or cat that would have required a few extra hands. It was when I considered step three in my plan that my face registered concern.

I was thinking about sending home a bottle of pills or some good tasting liquid and let the owner treat this snake in the privacy of his own home, when I recollected one fact from reptiles medicine. Reptiles do not absorb antibiotics given by mouth.

I was compelled to give my patient several injections of antibiotics over the course of the next ten days.

The first injection was easier than I imagined. The python contracted his powerful muscles along the length of his body as if a blast of cold wind shot underneath his tight fitting coat of scales. Nothing more. Maybe the continual gentle stroking of the snakes head by his master had a strong sedative affect, or maybe it was a lack of pain receptors in that area of the body, or perhaps it was that the pain was gone before the brain found out about it. I didn't know, I was just pleased it went well.

I informed the owner about the extra visits, which he agreed to. Then I informed my staff, who responded as if I had lost my mind all over again. I was pleased, because I had found a new fascination in the animal kingdom.

At each visit, I began questioning the owner about his hobby. Each question yielded new facts. The snake with the abscess was only one of many. He had over a dozen snakes of different species – he enjoyed having them. I asked him about caring for his snakes. He was knowledgeable about reptiles husbandry, and he provided me with many interesting facts about them. He also had a wife who was due to have a baby. She came with him on the last visit. She smiled when I asked her if she was afraid of her husband's hobby.

I asked her about feeding the snakes.

"That's his job," she said. "But it's interesting to watch."

It was during this conversation that the answer to the mystery of the abscesses surfaced. The Burmese python had a peculiar feeding habit. He would eat only live rats, not dead ones, and he would coil his body around the rat with the last 1/3 of his body. That's where the abscesses were. It was then that I realized how the snake received the lumps. The rats, his food, bit him.

The python was bitten by what he consumed.

The snake recovered from his experience, but I did not. I was bitten by this new exotic medicine. Several years later, reptiles became a popular part of my practice. People from many miles away now bring and assortment of turtles, iguanas, lizards, and a variety of snakes to see the veterinarian who will treat reptiles.

All this happened because I listened to someone with a problem and I learned from the snake who was bitten by what he consumed.

9

C.C.'S JUNGLE WORLD

Birds, lizards, snakes, and even salamanders get sick. I discovered that fast in my new position as adviser and health specialist for the Cloverbelt Pet Store. My knowledge, limited in these areas, was expanded by extensive reading and numerous telephone calls to university specialists for information about exotics. Trial and error wouldn't do for long, so I planned a trip to visit several successful pet stores in a large metropolitan area.

I had already learned that housing, environment, and nutrition played key roles in keeping exotics healthy – now to see these in practice.

Dan, the pet store fish specialist, was my companion on this learning adventure. He, too, was looking for more information. I was thankful my responsibilities did not include the fish. Our trip took us to two vastly different stores.

First, we drove to a suburban strip mini-mall where we located a new pet super-store. The freshly painted yellow parking strips still looked wet on the unmarred black asphalt where we parked. While waiting for the store to open, we peered inside and watched employees stock the shelves for the customers. We could see promotional posters on the walls that advertised premier cat food and specialty bird treats.

Once inside, we were drawn to a large-screen video that instructed owners about proper puppy feeding. Nearby, stacked high, were bags and cans of the puppy food promoted on the video. We watched momentarily and walked on.

We saw colorful plastic baskets stacked at tip-toe-height with a sign that said "for your shopping convenience." Attractive displays were present at every turn. Employees were smartly dressed with T-shirts bearing the store name boldly imprinted front-and-back. They worked intently without looking up as we walked by.

We toured the store, our pace leisurely museum-like. We viewed birds and snakes, amphibians and turtles, gerbils and rabbits, species after species. Some were housed singly, others in groups. Each cage was ultravioletly lit and antiseptically clean.

In the reptile wing of the store, our walking pace slowed to a crawl as we gazed at reptile after reptile, each in a 10 gallon aquarium. Row after row of tanks screened on the top for customer safety, and identically astro-turf lined on the bottom for reptile comfort. A computer printed tag gave each reptile a scientific name, and marked the price necessary to acquire the valuable contents – all with the customer in mind.

I studied each aquarium intently, and took detailed notes. Our tour of two hours took us back to the front of the store where Dan asked for a business card. We left impressed.

Our next stop took us downtown. We drove beyond the shopping centers and neighborhoods of identical houses, and then past brick stores with colorful awnings. We drove into a neighborhood of graffiti colored walls and closed business doors. No shoppers strolled the streets and few cars were parked curb side.

I parked the car and locked it good. I double checked the address we were given. A sign at that address said "Marine Aquatics," but the door was bolted shut. I turned to leave, but Dan, who didn't appear to notice the hostile environment we were parked in, walked to a door nearby that said "C.C. Jungle World." Graffiti from the outside wall spilled into the entryway of a small pet shop. This was not on our tour, but that didn't stop Dan from marching inside.

"When does Marine Aquatics open?" asked Dan.

"Not till noon," said a middle aged black man wearing a fish net shirt.

I looked at my watch, a 90-minute wait.

"Can we come in and look around your store?"

"Sure can, I'm C.C. and dis is my Jungle World."

We entered a twelve-by-twelve room that housed the entire contents of C.C.'s Jungle World. Cages covered every available space, from floor to above eye sight. Old paint peeled off the walls in places. The ceiling tiles were yellow-white with age, but displayed an elegance of former times. The smells of pine litter and animal foods hung in the air, and the sounds of birds screeching reverberated from the high ceiling.

We squeezed down two narrow isles of cages filled with an assortment of mammals, birds and reptiles. No name tags marked the cages, but an occasional faded piece of paper marked its worth.

We spent several minutes bumping into each other as we made our way around the shop, staring at cockatoos, love birds, an Amazon parrot, chinchillas, a pair of monkeys, several large iguanas, and a variety of geckos. Four German shepherd puppies played in a small wire cage blocking the back center isle.

We finished our brief circular survey of C.C.'s Jungle World in a dark corner behind the door. A brass incense burner spit out smoke with an exotic Asian odor.

In that corner was a glass cage that housed a large Burmese Reticulated Python. He lay coiled in the back of his cage – head resting on a bark-less tree branch. His eyes fixed in a straight-ahead gaze at me. A faded price tag of $499.00 was stuck to the glass.

"He's quite a snake ain't he," said C.C. "Thirteen feet long."

"What do you feed him?" I asked.

"Rabbits mostly, but sometimes I thro him a kid or two. Don't see any on the street do ya?" A big grin exposing two perfect rows of ivory teeth fills his round face.

C.C. then gave us a guided first-rate tour of his jungle world. He pointed to each animal, all his favorites. First on his list were the pair of warning birds clothed in brilliant iridescent green plumage.

"Dey warn the animals of danger," he said.

The pair of monkeys was rare, the gecko mean, and the Tokay lizard tame.

"Angora rabbits are de best," he said. "Dey calm when you hold them. Birds you gotta buy from Miami, dey are the best. Healthy and tame, but you pay a good price."

"Des are love birds, but I don't know why. Dey mean – see the eye on my cockatiel – love bird did dat – pecked it out – de are mean."

"Des are young myna birds – talking birds. Dey learn fast – kids teach them – dey swear at them – myna swear right back. I tell the boys don't come in here – you spoil my birds." He is not mad, but grinning.

"Dis young myna don't speak now – he will soon. The African grey – he speaks."

C.C. finishes the tour and asks for our business card. "I'll come visit you sometime," he says. "I'm moving my store up the street soon – more room."

He flashes us his big smile. We thank him and leave.

Robert Pope

At the end of the day I reflect on what I have seen. The mini-mall's complete convenience seems so opposite the cramped compact Jungle World of C.C. teeming with animal life. If I was a customer, the mini-mall store would be the place for me, but what if I had scales or feathers or fur? I conclude that C.C. Jungle world would be the place. He knows each animal by name and habit – the good and the bad – they are his and he accepts them. He knows their needs and they are under his special personal care. He is a keeper who cares.

Sometimes I complain because my world is not astro-turf lined, brightly-lit, and antiseptically-clean. Sometimes I complain because I don't find life lined up in uniform displays for my convenience. Sometimes I complain because I must live next to love birds who aren't loving, and I must deal with the geckos of this world. I feel cramped and out of sorts. I don't like the smell of incense, pine bedding makes me sneeze, and screeching sounds hurt my ears. But in all this I know that the Creator who made me also knows best how to care for me.

chapter
10

THE HORSE TRIAL

If life was a card game, then Frank Anderson must have been dealt a lousy hand. He was a farmer, of sorts, and lived just inside the county line. His livestock, mostly beef cows, horses, and ponies, grazed the pasture in the summer and huddled in a lean-to-shelter of a barn in the winter.

I don't know what Frank did for a living. I know he didn't milk cows, or grow much in the way of crops, or work out. He was always there. I know he was poor, and he drank a bit, and his face was often two days past a shave. He mumbled when he talked and pushed the end of words through his nose, giving them elongated significance.

Summer was the only season I knew Frank worked. He took his ponies to the local fairs and gatherings and gave pony rides to children for a dollar.

My first encounter with Frank was through the police department. Frank called the police because a few of his beef cows were dead. Frank screamed fowl play, and the police summoned the country humane officer who had played out these cards before. It was Frank's way to get a veterinarian to come, and the county to foot the bill.

Frank did care for his animals – he gave them the best he had – it just wasn't very much. His horses always thinned out during winter, but when spring and green pastures returned, they would round out again.

One cold December evening Frank called about an accident that happened to one of his ponies. I arrived to find the pony with his side sliced open, and a portion of intestines hanging to the ground. Frank would not have the pony put down. He wanted me to save the poor beast, so for two hours I performed surgery in a cold, dark barn with Frank holding a 60 watt bulb as the only source of heat and light. I crudely attempted to put back the misplaced intestines and suture the layers of abdominal muscles. The pony died, and he paid with a load of firewood.

"Doesn't matter, we had to tryyy," said Frank.

Frank was like that.

Years passed and I lost touch with Frank. I retired from large animal work with its country calls, and I focused my energy on dogs and cats. I heard rumors that Frank lost his farm. Some shrewd-talking card shark weaseled him into a loan he couldn't repay, and the family farm was lost in the transaction.

When I did hear from Frank, he was in big trouble. "I needdd your help, Doc – you're the only one can help me nowww."

"What's the problem?" I asked.

"I lost my farm, so we moved across the county line. They took my horses; said I wern't caring for them; said they had no waterr, but they had water; said I had to carry fresh water in pails, and they got plenty of good water in the creek, back of the barn. Don't understand it. I did nothin' wronggg."

"You gotta help me, Doc," Frank pleaded.

As we talked the circumstances unfolded. It seems the other county didn't know Frank and his ways. When he moved to their jurisdiction with what was left of his horses and ponies, he continued life as usual – thin, hairy animals in winter and well rounded livestock come summer.

Someone blew the whistle on Frank for in-humane treatment of animals, and the humane society seized his horses. Frank wanted me to examine the horses, and represent him in the court battle that was sure to follow.

I agreed, somewhat reluctantly. I knew this man, and I knew he would not willingly neglect his animals. He was either very down on his luck, or the humane officer was wrong. I was puzzled.

I contacted the county humane officer and arranged to see the horses. We drove to the farm where Frank's horses had been deported, and I spent several hours examining them for signs of abuse or neglect. The horses looked like Frank's – no fat, but also no abuse. Two ponies were nursing young foals, and they looked healthy. Frank had been caring for his animals the way Frank always cared for them. I took some blood samples and made some detailed notes.

Then I visited the farm where Frank housed his animals. There I saw hay of poor quality, water in buckets placed here and there, shell corn spilled on the ground, and a lean-to-shelter of a barn. It looked liked Frank's old place transported across the county line.

These horses deserved better, but they were not neglected or inhumanely treated. I took photographs to support my views.

Frank was accused of neglect to animals, and a court date was set. I would be the witness for the defense in this sad tale of events.

I met with two poker-faced court appointed lawyers for Frank's defense, and I explained to them Frank's ways as best I could. They told me if I played the cards right, Frank would be acquitted, if not he would be charged with neglect to animals. After our brief meeting, they nodded simultaneous approval of my position, closed their leather briefcases, and left me to do the worrying.

On the day of the court trial, my mind was filled with scenes of television courtroom trials, my only experience. I told myself it couldn't be that bad. But how could I convey to a jury of 12 individuals that Frank's animal care, although not high quality, was far from neglect. He had met the basics of animal husbandry: food, water, shelter. I just didn't believe I could convince others of his good intentions.

A court official ushered me into a room where I waited most of the day without being summoned to testify. I went home exhausted from nervousness. But the next morning as the first witness, I was called into the courtroom, sworn in, and ascended the witness stand. From this vantage point I surveyed my position.

The jury was seated to my right, mostly out of my view. The stern faced judge was perched behind me. Frank's black-jack-card-playing defense attorneys were positioned in front on one side, and the prosecuting attorneys with an assortment of experts on the other side. The court room was buzzing with all the excitement of a Las Vegas casino. The judge pounded his gavel and called for order.

Questions for the defense were fired off like rapidly played cards. I answered question after question as truthfully as I could.

"The horses are thin," I said. "You can see from the pictures," I said, ". . . Here are the results of my physical examination. Here are the results of my laboratory tests."

The defense rested. I took a moment to catch my breath.

The prosecution began with their questions – detailed questions about my professional qualifications. Was I an expert in horses? Was I an expert in nutrition? Was I a qualified veterinarian? How many years had I practiced veterinary medicine? Did I have any advanced degrees?

I recognized two of the men seated next to the prosecuting attorney (whispering in his ear). They were expert veterinarians – high rollers from the University. They had played cards before, and they set the stakes. I was the small-town, small-time player in a high-stakes game.

I became acutely conscious of my every word, and started to feel that my luck had run out. But I couldn't cash in my chips and leave from the table. They tried to changed my meaning. What I said was thin, they wanted to call emaciated. What I said was adequate, they wanted to called marginal. What I called provided for they called neglect.

The questions became a shadow in my mind, then a pause in the proceedings. I closed my eyes, and now I saw clearly the next scene. I was looking at Frank in prison through the bars. He sat at the foot of his metal cot, his face in need of a two day shave. He turned to me, and I could hear him say, "They got it in for me, Doc, but we had to tryy."

Suddenly it was over. I was done. I was excused.

It took several days before I heard the results of the trial. The proceedings had continued long after I was done. Frank was acquitted of all charges of animal abuse.

I never saw Frank after the trial, nor have I seen him since.

Life is more than luck, just good or bad. Somehow I had been able to deal Frank a few cards from a new deck, I hope it has given him a new stake on life. I may never know, but I know I had to try.

chapter

11

A REAL MAN

I met a real man one Saturday who was bear-claw strong and pine-tree tall. He wore mud stained jeans, a red and green checked flannel shirt, and leather work shoes. He's in the construction business – a man's business. He can talk tough and drink and smoke, but none of this makes him a real man.

When I entered his house he gave me a firm hand shake. I remember thinking, "He has a solid grip on things, maybe my job will be not so bad." He led me to the kitchen where a bay window and sliding glass door gave an open air view to the back yard and distant horse barn. His wife sat cross-legged on the kitchen floor, her head in the palms of her hands propped up by her elbows. Their dog, Kristin, lay next to her.

We talked for a while, he and his wife and I. We talked of mostly man things, hunting Up North where man's country begins. He told me it started north of Highway 64, Wisconsin's Northwoods. We talked about downhill skiing, snow and snowmobiling, ice and ice fishing. We talked about being in business, about health insurance, and tough times making a business go. We talked all this, man talk, he and his wife and I.

Then, after some time, we had to become serious about the business at hand. Unpleasant business, but timely. Kristen was 18 years old and failing. She was his wife's dog before their marriage, a faithful companion and her only child. The dog's eyes were gray-white from cataracts. The hair was brittle and falling out in patches. The rich black and brown colors, distinct Shepherd markings, had faded white in spots. Lost was her youthful enthusiasm. Her emaciated body displayed all her ribs, and her back legs, now, were so weak from arthritis that she couldn't rise without help. Medication no longer helped. The long battle was lost.

I came to put her to rest, to sleep. His wife held the dog's head, stroking her between the ears while we talked some more. He left the room for a brief moment. I saw redness in his eyes when he returned.

63

I gave the aging Shepherd a heavy dose of tranquilizer first, because it was easier that way, and because she would feel no pain.

"This will take 10 or 15 minutes, then I will give her the rest," I said.

He and his wife nodded. They were in no hurry. They knew this was best for Kristen, but not for them.

When the time passed, I injected the euthanasia solution in the long leg vein. Now this real man left the room again, while his wife hugged the dog tight. When the job was finished he returned, but spoke nothing. He picked up the now limp and lifeless body of their dog, and carried her outside.

I offered to help.

"No, just stay with my wife for a few minutes," he said.

His wife and I, silent, watched him through the large kitchen window as he carried their dog to a freshly dug grave. He took a long time, his movements mechanical and slow. When he returned, tears now flowing freely, he hugged his wife.

I watched them grieve as if on the other side of the double paned kitchen window. But I was drawn into their grief with my own tears. (I usually shed them when nobody is looking – after I'm gone – you know – strong – like a man).

There I was, a potted plant, in their kitchen watching their sadness and fighting back my tears. I wanted to leave, but I could not move.

Then this man, sensing my presence and sadness did something I will never forget. First he shook my hand with that same firm hand shake he gave me when I came. Then he said, "Thank you for coming and for staying with my wife." When he saw my tears, now watering the spot where I stood, he gave me a bear hug.

I choked out my good-byes and left by the door I had entered.

I had met a real man.

* * * * * * * *

I read about another real man. He wore sandals on his feet. His father was a carpenter, in the construction business. On one busy day He was told about the death of His close friend. The Scriptures record these few words, packed with the meaning of true manhood: "Jesus wept." (John 11:35).

chapter

12

RYKER, A TRUE FAIRY TALE

Once upon a time in the North woods of Wisconsin, lived a very nice young man. He had many friends and that made him happy, but even so, he was very lonely. His many friends told him to find a wonderful companion so he wouldn't be lonely any more.

So the nice young man searched and searched for a wonderful companion. One day he found just the right companion, a small beautiful male German Shepherd puppy.

"He would make a wonderful companion," said the nice young man.

So the nice young man took the beautiful puppy home, and he promised to love him and take care of him.

"I will have to give my puppy a good name," said the nice young man. "I want him to grow up to be big and strong, I think I'll call him Ryker."

And so it was that the beautiful puppy became Ryker, a wonderful companion. And the nice young man wasn't lonely any more. This is the beginning of our story.

Ryker grew and grew as all puppy dogs do. He grew up to be big and strong. Ryker's owner loved him and was proud of his wonderful companion. He smiled with great pleasure as he told his many friends about his wonderful companion. They were very happy for the nice young man.

However, as Ryker grew, his attitude about life changed. He became big and strong, all right, but he thought he should be in charge. He would show his teeth and growl when he didn't get his way. The many friends were surprised and shocked by Ryker's attitude. They were afraid of Ryker and stayed away from him.

This pleased Ryker very much because it made him feel important. He was now big and strong and in charge. One day Ryker tried his new strength and importance out at the veterinary office. But the good doctor and the kind technician did not back away from him as other people did. So Ryker growled louder and showed more teeth. This still did not give him the control that made him feel important. Then he lunged at the kind technician and good doctor, barking and bearing his teeth in an attempt to bite them severely for their lack of understanding. This caused the good doctor and kind assistant to cringe in fear.

The nice young man was embarrassed and could do nothing to stop his wonderful companion. He told him he was a bad dog, but Ryker knew he had complete control.

The nice young man continued to love and care for his wonderful companion, but when Ryker did not want to do something, all he had to do was growl and show his teeth in disapproval, and nice young man could not force him to do so. Ryker was very happy – he had control.

One day, many years later, Ryker's eyes became bad, so the nice young man took him to see the good doctor and the kind technician at the veterinary clinic.

"Ryker has a bad disease," said the good doctor. "He is going blind because his eyes do not have enough tears."

"What can be done?" said the nice young man.

"Oh," said the good doctor, "it is easy to control the disease, but it cannot be cured. If you place these drops of healing medicine in your wonderful companion's eyes twice a day, he will get well."

"How long will I have to do this for Ryker?" said the nice young man.

"This must be done every day from now on," said the good doctor, "or his eyes will dry out and he will go blind."

The kind technician nodded her head in approval and handed the healing medicine to the nice young man.

"What if Ryker doesn't want me to put the drops in his eyes?" said the nice young man.

"Oh, that would be terrible!" said the good doctor.

The kind technician nodded her head in approval, and said, "Terrible!"

And that's exactly what did happen. Ryker big and strong and in control, would growl and show his teeth when the nice young man tried to put the healing medicine in Ryker's eyes. The nice young man pleaded and begged and cajoled Ryker. He told Ryker how serious and how important and how necessary the healing medicine was. He told Ryker he loved him and didn't want him to go blind.

Some days Ryker would allow the nice young man to put the healing medicine in his eyes. This felt good and made the itch go away. But mostly Ryker would not listen, because he was big and strong and in control, and he would decide when the medicine could be put in his eyes.

All this made the nice young man very sad, but what could he do for his wonderful companion? He told his many friends about Ryker's problem. They did not know what to do either.

Ryker's eyes continued to get worse and worse until one day he became blind. All this time Ryker remained big and strong and in control. All this time the nice young man would beg and plead and cajole, and be sad when Ryker said no. And all this time the good doctor said, "What else can I do?" And all this time the kind technician nodded her head. And all this time the many friends did not know what to do either.

One day something very bad happened. Ryker was being big and strong and in control. He had said no to the healing medicine. Ryker went out into the busy street where he wasn't supposed to go. The nice young man had told Ryker over and over again not to go into the street, because he loved Ryker and he was his wonderful companion. But Ryker couldn't see and he didn't listen, and a very large truck hit Ryker.

When the nice young man told his many friends and the good doctor and the kind technician about what happened to Ryker, they were all sad because the nice young man had lost his wonderful companion. But they all shook their heads from side to side and said, "What could anybody do?"

Every fairy tale should have a moral. The moral of the story about Ryker is this. It's okay to be big and strong, it's not good to always be in control, and it's bad to show your teeth and growl. Always getting your own way can lead to bad things. Who wants a wonderful companion that acts like Ryker?

chapter

13

DAILY DANGERS

"How can you do that? Have you ever been hurt? What about rabies? Don't you get bit?"

When I'm asked questions about the safety of my job, I answer them gladly because they usually come from owners with pets that don't bite, and I never fail to give credit to my staff who protect me from scalpel-sharp teeth and needle-like claws. But sometimes the questions cause my mind to do an instant replay of past dangerous moments.

I have a few injuries and a scar or two to show for my work (like the fine line at the corner of my right eye inflicted by a horn from a cow), but these have been minor. Besides, it's not the injuries that are bad. It's the near misses – the serious things that could-have-been, but then, they didn't. These events are etched into my memory like video clips.

Once I was chased by an angry Black Angus bull, and another time I nearly lost my ear from a kicking-bronco with long horns. But it was one dog in particular that kept me in constant fear. His name was Ryker, and he occupied the body of a 90 pound male German Shepherd. He had an attitude, and the muscle to back it up.

As an eight week old puppy, Ryker was not a problem, but he developed an attitude as he matured into adulthood. I tried the usual bribes with dog bone treats, but he didn't fall for that ruse. I tried the gentle touch and voice. I tried the tough-guy approach with the firm "Be Good, NOW" voice. He grew increasingly apprehensive of me and my office with each visit.

One day Ryker took total control and pinned my assistant and me against the wall. Snarling, he stood upright on his back legs, and looked me in the eye like an angry football halfback ready to take a swing. His face was inches from my throat. His canine teeth seemed yard-stick long, and ready to strike.

The owner, although he possessed bench-pressed muscles on a basketball-tall frame, was helpless to call off his dog. Eventually, for reasons unknown to me, Ryker backed down and walked away. But his attitude from that moment on said to me, "I've got you now, Doctor!" And he was right. Because from that day, just the sound of his name turned my bones to jell-o until death parted him from his body several years later.

I remember only one time when I truly regretted my chosen profession.

It had already been a Ryker-like day. I was kicked at by a cow, growled at by a diminutive dog, and slash-attacked by a cat. I was feeling sorry for myself long before my visit to the doctor's office.

I was waiting in an exam room of the local medical center for the doctor to inspect my knee, an injury inflicted by a horse two weeks earlier.

The room served as an all-purpose treatment area for minor emergencies, quick exams, and blood collections. A thin pull-across curtain divided the room into two areas. Nurses walked briskly in and out because the room also acted as a main thoroughfare to other parts of the building.

I was seated on a padded examination table, one of those with the stiff white roll-across-paper. My legs dangled over the edge giving my injured knee some rest. The curtain veiled half of the room from my view.

My eyes walked around the room, scrutinizing everything. They settled on the long counter behind me busy with medical supplies. This counter was the main artery of the clinic, providing the supplies used most and needed often. It was furnished with stainless steel trays of instruments and glass jars marked "cotton swabs" and "tongue depressors" (a commodity I have little use for); a brown plastic alcohol dispenser similar to my own; an assortment of gauze sponges and band-aid like pads; and several boxes of brightly colored blood collection tubes. A slight antiseptic odor hung in the air dampened by a trace of perfume from a nearby nurse.

At one end of the counter was the ECG crash cart station. (The ECG machine is the heart of any good medical facility, a machine I couldn't afford). The cart was chest high and steel bars cradled the machine tightly like a giant rib cage. A clear plastic dust cloth draped over the vital knobs of the ECG like a protective skin, leaving exposed only the trailing paper from its last use. I reached over and touched the plastic cloth, and ran my index finger over the knobs.

It was then that I began to daydream, and let my thought drift to a profession with less danger and more respect.

"I could have been a pediatrician," I imagined. "It's a lot safer, more lucrative, and I could enjoy being a kid's doctor. I'd be appreciated, too. Children give smiles when they feel better, and parents are appreciative."

So my thoughts drifted around the room.

Unexpectedly I was pulled from my daydreaming by a sporting event played out before me on the other side of the curtain. I never saw the players in action, and there was no sportscaster for blow by blow description, but my ears snatched up every sound as if I had a box office seat.

"This won't hurt a bit," said the nurse who was the source of the perfume, "I just need a little blood sample for some tests. Be very still and don't move."

"Eooowwww eeeee, eooowwwww-eeeee!"

The shrieking echoed out across the thin barrier, vibrating my knee, and the curtain undulated in-and-out-back-and-forth as various limbs and body parts protruded into my side of the room.

"I need some help in here!" shouted the nurse.

Two voices came to her rescue, one with husky tones. "Ouch, he bit me," cried the perfume voice. I've got him now," said the husky one.

Indistinct noises and curtain movements continued for three or four minutes until I heard a final whimper. Then the curtain hung still. The action ended as abruptly as it started, and all the commotion retreated.

Seconds later one exhausted nurse trudged past me into the lab carrying a purple topped blood tube in her left hand and kissing tenderly the index finger of her right hand.

I decided, "I don't have it so bad, Charging black bulls, Ryker, and Wild horses were nothing compared to this."

But there are some genuine dangers in my profession, dangers that I don't talk to clients about or daydream about. These dangers are the silent, unseen, and overlooked dangers of veterinary medical practice. Organisms so small that it takes powerful microscopes and special colored dyes to see them. Bacteria, fungal spores, or viruses can do more damage to a body than Ryker's fangs or an angry bulls' hooves.

Rabies is a virus, and it's dangerous because the symptoms can be mistaken for many different diseases, especially in the early stages. In 25 years of practice, I've witnessed firsthand, cases of rabies in a dog, a horse, and cow. Each one could have been something else. It's easy to become exposed by sticking fingers in the mouth of a drooling dog looking for a bone, or by concluding that a stiff horse has tetanus. It's also easy to mistake the bellowing of rabid cow for a bovine in labor. It's easy, and then it's too late, because you've been exposed.

More than once, I waited anxiously for test results from a potentially rabid animal.

There is no cure for rabies like the cure for daydreams or Ryker dogs. There is only prevention.

That's why I'm in the exam room waiting for a nurse to administer my rabies vaccination (the same prevention I give my four legged patients). It's been several years since the daydreaming episode.

I can smell the clinical antiseptic mixed with a touch of perfume. I look around the room. It's changed some. The pull across curtain is gone, replaced by a solid wall that doesn't let the sounds around. The bottles and blood tubes are all in place, and the ECG machine is waiting to be used. (I now have a veterinary version of the same machine).

Life is not so bad, I think. I have bad days and bad times, but my animal patients are generally receptive to my help.

As the nurse injects my forearm with the rabies vaccine, I notice a Band-Aid on her hand. I think about asking her for details, but I change my mind. Instead, I muster up a special closure and say, "I hope your day has an extra dose of goodness."

MOSINEE VETERINARY CLINIC

Robert Pope

chapter

14

SNAKE OILS

The call came too late, too late to save her, I thought as I stared at the large 1400 pound Holstein cow. She was cut down in the prime of her production.

"She's one of my best milkers, I can't afford to loose her," said David.

"It always seems to happen to the best," I said.

David was a good dairyman, my age and my height. I could look him in the eye when we talked.

I examined the cow closely to locate the cause of her problem. She lay down, unable to rise. Her eyes were glazed, and her head swung around the side of her body, limp-like. Her heart was slow and pulsed an irregular beat.

I continued my examination, and I worked my way to the back of the cow where I discovered the cause of her illness. When I squirted the sample of milk into my hand, it was watery with flakes.

"You were right to worry, Dennis, she has toxic mastitis – and a bad case," I told him straight out.

"I'll give her the best medicine I have, but you know the rest is up to her."

His eyes met mine, and he shook his head from side to side.

I administered antibiotics, anti-inflammatory drugs, and medicine to help fight the toxemia. I left.

Toxic mastitis is a severe condition of the udder in which bacteria release toxins into the blood of the cow. It's like a bad case of blood poisoning. Worse than that, David's cow was down, unable to stand – a serious condition for a large bovine. Even if she survived the toxemia, but wasn't on her feet in 24 hours, permanent paralysis would set in. It would be a terrible loss.

In cases like this, I would turn my thoughts to cure-alls, ("All's" I need is a cure), a veterinary panacea, a silver bullet certain to work.

For David's cow I had none, and I had done all I could. For now, I would attend to other cases and check back with my patient in the afternoon.

Robert Pope

A call from David came a few hours later.

"She got up!" he said, "After you left a man came by selling a new treatment. He called it *Kickapoo Joy Juice*. He gave her a shot and in ten minutes she was on her feet. Now she's eating. It sure is a miracle cure – made from milk antibodies and fortified with vitamins. Just thought you'd like to know. Maybe you should get some. Thanks for your help, anyway, Doc."

I paused to reflect what had happened. A traveling salesman's unproven elixir brings instant relief to David's ailing cow, while my prescription inoculations given four hours previously had no effect? Why does *Kickapoo Joy Juice* get the credit? Medical magic? Coincidence? Good fortune? Charm? What makes people crave a miracle cure for cows? For sickness? For life?

I ruminated on these questions.

Years ago patented medicines were sold by peddlers that had claims of curing "all that ails." They were called snake oils. The dictionary defines a snake oil as "any one of various preparations advertised as medicine supposed to cure certain ailments such as rheumatism, colds, or baldness. Formally sold by peddlers posing as scientific doctors, or the like."

I have seen many modern products sold as snake oils for animals and people. They have a list of traits in common:

1. Secret or special ingredients.
2. Can be used to cure any condition
3. Must be used according to complicated directions
4. Must be repeated continuously.
5. Have complicated, almost scientific explanations for why they work.
6. Are expensive

If the product fails to work, the fault in not in the product, but in the user. Advice from the snake oil peddler becomes: not enough treatments, not enough product, not applied correctly. Use more – do it again – do it again. People still believe, and snake oils get the credit.

Why is the snake oil charmed?

A wise professor gave his class of veterinary students the following advice: "Remember," he said, "when you graduate and begin practice that 10% of the animals you treat will die despite your good care. Do your best for these animals, but don't be discouraged. Remember also that 10% of the animals you treat will benefit greatly from your help – these will recover – so treat them properly. The other 80%? They will get better by themselves – so whatever you do, don't mess them up!"

Snake oils smooth to recovery the 80% that becomes healthy themselves.

Everyone wants a cure for problems. Everyone wants to believe in something that will oil troubles away. Problems with health, problems with money, problems with people, problems with problems – everyone looks for that magic snake oil cure for life.

I've heard some people peddle health, religion, or financial success like a snake oil, guaranteed to change your life for the better. "Just do this often enough," they say. "Just follow these special rules," they say. "Just give enough," they say. Just believe enough, just . . . just . . . just. . . snake oil. And like the shed skin of a snake, any healing, any change, any success, is only one scale deep.

There is help available for life, and it's found as close as a pocket or purse. It's available for everyone, rich or poor, young or old. It's not magic, There's no scientific formula or secret remedy for finding it, no complicated or difficult treatment plan to follow, no expensive price to be paid. It's freely given. Life's Problems aren't shed like a skin, and they can't be oiled into just slipping away. You can find the instructions written on the face of every coin or dollar bill. How easy it is to forget our country motto, "In God We Trust."

chapter

15

All I NEEDED, I LEARNED FROM TANGLES WITH PORCUPINES

It's 5:00 P.M., early Fall, on a Wednesday. I'm tired because it's been an on-the-run kind of day. I'm just leaving for home when the telephone rings. I'm tempted not to answer, but I do, forcing a cheerful "hello."

"Oh, you're still there, can I bring my dogs in – they just tangled with a porcupine?"

"Dogs? As in more than one?" I ask.

"Yes, two, they got loose today and were running in the woods."

"Bring them right in."

Two dogs, that's double trouble, I think and talk, half to myself and half to the clinic walls as I prepare the instruments and medications I need to remove the quills.

Who would think that a creature I seldom see could cause so much trouble? Porcupines living deep in the pine forest. They climb trees and eat green leaves and tree bark. Even hunters count them as a nuisance. The flesh is edible but nobody considers it tasty.

Why are dogs fascinated with these slow moving relatives of rats? Why am I the lucky one who gets to remove the devastating results of this "tangle with a porcupine?" And why does every phone call about porcupines start with the same expression, "my dog tangled with . . .?" Questions I Ponder while I wait.

I've never personally witnessed one of these tangles, and neither do owners. Mostly it happens at night. However it happens, I'm told on good authority, the poor dog doesn't stand a chance, because the porcupine backs into its victim.

Now I have a pair of tangles on their way to my hospital. The porcupine is the winner, and the dog the loser, but what does that make me?

After a thirty minute wait, the owner arrives. He is young and tall and lean, but with a sheepish grin of guilt on his face. He is inexperienced in these porcupine matters. So are his two collie-like dogs with a full snouts full of quills. No guilt written there.

I put the dogs on my exam table and begin by tranquilizing them. I inject a solution into the long leg vein and wait for them to relax.

I remember the first time I took a close look at one of the porcupine quills under the microscope. Each quill possesses thousands of tiny backwards pointing barbs, barely visible. Magnified they look menacing, but removed from the victim they seem almost harmless until you put them somewhere. Then they stick like velcro.

The dogs now relax, and I begin the tedious process of pulling quills one at a time.

There is no great skill required to pull quills – there are no great porcupine quill removing veterinarians. The procedure is simple enough: grab each quill close to where it enters the skin and pull firmly and quickly. I use my favorite porcupine quill-pulling hemostat, when I can find it, but a needle nosed pliers also works well – in a pinch.

I hand an instrument to the owner. The guilt on his face has vanished, and now he has watched me for fifteen minutes; that makes him experienced in porcupine quill matters. We both pull quills.

After all the visible quills are gone, I meticulously move my fingers back and forth, feeling for broken stubs. These I work out by pushing the quill forward until the sharp tip spears my finger, mingling my fresh blood with the dried blood from the victim. The broken stubs come easily once exposed in this way. Satisfied I've removed the last pieces, I reverse the sedation and send the dogs home to contemplate the error of their ways.

One week later, it's 5:00pm. I'm tired, and it's been another on-the-run kind of a day. I'm ready to go home when the telephone rings. I'm tempted not to answer it, but I do.

"Hi, it's me again, can I bring my dog in to remove quills? One of them has tangled with a porcupine again. Just one dog, the lighter haired one."

"Bring him in."

I wait.

Most dogs will have one, and only one tangle with a porcupine. The pain of the quills is memory enough to avoid these armored tanks traveling in reverse. I couldn't imagine why this dog was mesmerized by them.

The owner arrives and he apologizes for his dog. The dog grins at me with his a snout full of quills. I put the dog on my exam table, and begin by tranquilizing him. I inject a solution into the long leg vein and wait for him to relax.

We pull quills and talk. He's an expert now.

I reverse the sedation, and send the dog home to contemplate the error of his ways, hoping he'll learn this time.

It's 5:00pm, about one week later. I'm tired. I've been tired for three weeks. The telephone rings, and I answer it.

"It's me. He has quills."

"I guessed as much, see you soon."

I wait.

Most dogs are intelligent animals, I believe. True stories tell amazing things some dogs can do. Look at Lassie, and she was a Collie. One dog I know can add, subtract, multiply, and divide any number with and answer between 1 and 9 (for a biscuit of course, the dog is not stupid). Other dogs, of average intelligence, can perform many phenomenal tricks, some for no treat at all. This dog can't seem to learn a simple lesson.

The owner arrives with his dog and the quills. The dog prances into the examination room and gives me a happy look, a sort of victory smile. Quills decorate his face like battle trophies, more than last time.

I reach to pick him up, being careful not to get pricked, but in one effortless motion he jumps on top of the table. I reach for the dog's leg to inject the tranquilizer, but he extends it for me, placing his paw perfectly into my hand.

The owner and I laugh as we realize the twisted intelligence of his dog.

I would love to have a one-on-one conversation with this animal. He would tell me of his mission. He would, I believe, tell me about appointing himself the sole canine crusader against porcupines. He would talk about ridding the Northwoods of an armed nuisance. He would describe to me the thrill of the chase and the horrible obstacle to his success – all those nasty quills. Then he would thank me for providing a solution to the problem, and for painlessly removing the prickly quills.

Although I'll never have that one-on-one, this dog did teach me some valuable lessons about tangling with prickly porcupine-like problems. Here they are:

1. I often create my own problems.
2. When I'm all tangled up, it does little good to blame someone else for my trouble.
3. I should stay away from places where problems breed, like deep dark pine forests. If I'm looking for trouble-in the dark-I'm likely to encounter it.
4. At times problems just seem to back into me when I'm not looking.
5. I should put my armor on, because an ounce of prevention is worth a pound of quills.
6. I shouldn't rely on myself to untangle some problems, but trust in the help of others.

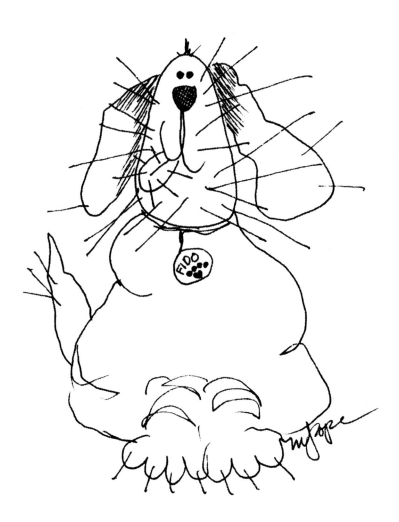

chapter
16

THE DECLAW

Mistakes, we all make them. Some mistakes hurt, some mistakes cost, some we forget as soon as they're over, others stick like glue to the mind for life. I still remember my first mistakes declawing cats, though I made them over 20 years ago.

The first cat I declawed wrong was my own gray tabby, Humpty-Dumpty. He tipped me off to my blunder. Little bumps where his claws used to be mysteriously appeared a few months after surgery. Then one day new, but grotesquely deformed claws exposed themselves. First the tips sprouted out, then the stems, like dandelions not fully uprooted.

Like many mistakes and most surgical errors, the correction proved more difficult than the original surgery. Unlike the nursery rhyme, I was able to put Humpty-Dumpty together again.

Once I discovered my error, I excavated my way through all my records to unearth any other declaw mistakes.

It was during this hunt that I discovered Charlie among my declaw disasters. Charlie, a short-haired black and white tom cat, belonged to Mrs. Drake, a petite elderly eccentric widow. They were kindred spirits, and possessed a zest for life with an independent vein that pulsed deep within their circulatory beings.

Part of Charlie's independent nature grew from his local reputation as a scrapper. Doing battle with the neighborhood intruders was serious business. Frequently he returned home victorious from these feline brawls for territory, but just as often the battles left wounds. Then it became Mrs. Drake's duty to bring Charlie in for repairs, but duty and independence often run counter-current.

She would make an appointment for 2:30 Tuesday afternoon, but show up at 4:00, or not at all, or on Wednesday at 2:30. Charlie couldn't be found, and she couldn't miss the opening day of the United Methodist Church bazaar. That was her nature. Somehow Charlie got the treatment he needed, and he seemed to understand his mistress's ways even if I didn't.

"Oh, that Charlie Cat, he's a bum," she would say. Then her wrinkled eyelids would pop open, exposing her half hidden irises. At the same time both corners of her mouth would move up to meet her pupils. It was as if both eyes and mouth were connected by a string and controlled by the puppeteer deep inside her.

Charlie was a pleasant patient. He remained calm during my examinations of poking and prodding hands, and he didn't flinch from my antibiotic injections. Maybe the teeth and claws from foes that entered his body like so many stray bullets were far more painful than my needles. Maybe he had become immune to the needle sting. I believe he understood my intentions were for his good.

Charlie used and needed his claws for military reasons. That's why I was surprised the day Mrs. Drake asked about declawing Charlie.

It was winter in Mosinee, and Mrs. Drake decided on a trip to Florida. Her daughter would care for Charlie as usual, but there was a problem. For short trips, Charlie stayed home, where his military maneuvers and territorial disputes remained regular. But this was not a trip, more of a vacation, as she called it. Plans were made for Charlie to stay at her daughter's house. That's what caused a dilemma.

"My daughter is concerned about Charlie Cat scratching her furniture," she said.

"I could declaw Charlie," I said, "but what would he do to defend himself after he got home?"

"Well, yes, but if I have Charlie declawed, then he couldn't scratch the furniture, and he could stay at my daughter's house, and I can go on my vacation, and I don't have to worry."

She was adamant.

"Maybe Charlie could be an inside cat when your return," I said. But even my own words sounded hollow.

I declawed Charlie, and Mrs. Drake took her vacation.

It was several months later when I heard from Mrs. Drake. Charlie was limping, and he had been out patrolling his boundaries.

I examined Charlie, but this time his infection originated from his own claws. Sharp bayonet tipped claws protruded from the skin. Bacteria invaded the area which became a ripe battle ground for infection. Now his feet were sore.

I told Mrs. Drake about my error, explaining in detail what I had done wrong, but it was like talking to wood.

"Oh, Dr. Pope, you're so clever to do that for my Charlie Cat. He's such a bum. He did fine at my daughters, but now when he needs his claws, they're coming back again.

Somehow I must have pulled a string, because in an instant my sin which was exposed was washed away and forgiven.

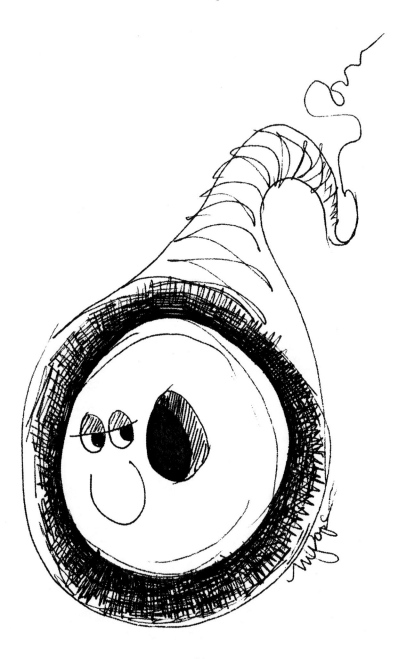

chapter
17

AMAZING BLOOD

People have had a love affair with man's manufacturing miracle, the automobile, since Henry Ford first placed the "Model T" in reach of the masses in 1908. Today over 340 million automobiles travel on the highways of the world. Automobile production in United States alone is over 6 million passenger cars annually.

This "miracle" does not compare to God's creative genius, however. His creations seem endless. As a surgeon operating on animals, I see firsthand God's manufacturing wonders. I depend upon the proper function and operation of the blood and circulatory system each time I pick up the scalpel.

Let's take a journey – a life journey. This is the journey of a red blood cell.

Manufacturing starts deep in the dark recesses of the bone marrow. This four ounce factory uses the raw materials of copper, iron, proteins and several vitamins, along with a "factory template" stem cell, to produce an oxygen carrying red blood cell. The process from start to finish is completed in seven days. In fact this storehouse can release 200 billion red cells daily into the circulation network. The blood squeezed from one pin-prick holds 5 million of these small cells.

So vast, this network consists of 100,000 miles of blood cell highway-like vessels: arteries, the out-going expressways; capillaries, the narrow connecting streets; and veins, the broad returning routes. Traffic here moves at interstate speed.

The tiny donut-shaped blood cell is pushed around the body one time a minute. It is squirted out of the heart, propelled through branching arteries of smaller and smaller size, squeezed through capillaries no wider than the cell itself, sucked and shoved through veins of larger and larger size, and finally deposited in the heart – only to be squirted out again.

There is more to life than the journey. The blood cells have a serious mission – the delivery of life giving oxygen to every cell in the body. And the blood cell is designed for just such a task. Packed inside each cell are 280 million molecules of oxygen-carrying hemoglobin. Hemoglobin attracts oxygen from the lungs like a magnet attracts metal. So crucial is this design that if oxygen were dissolved in blood, like sugar in water, a 20 pound beagle would need to double in size just to transport oxygen!

All this from one single blood cell. This oxygen delivering "Mission Impossible" is completed 170,000 times in the short 120 day life span of the blood cell.

What designing engineer's detailed blueprints produced this marvel? Certainly not chance. Only a Creator God possessing the highest powers of wisdom and knowledge could. What new safety devices need be installed, or what improvements need be made? None. What factory recalls or manufacturing mistakes need correcting? None. When I operate, what happens if this complex, well designed system fails? Disaster strikes a few minutes later.

As a veterinary surgeon, I depend daily upon the intricate inner-working details He has planned, and I am reminded that ". . . I am fearfully and wonderfully made . . . I know that full well." (Psalms 139:14-15).

BloodSisters

chapter
18

THE TRANSFUSION

Shadow is a timid Sheltie – distrustful of strangers, like many of that breed, but she is devoted to her owner. She comes to my clinic for routine vaccinations and checkups. Mehan, her sister, always accompanies her. Today she is alone, so I know it isn't a routine visit.

"Shadow isn't well. She's vomiting and won't eat." Her owner is a young man with round wire-rimmed glasses, heavy lenses, and a face to wear them well. He is in stark contrast to Shadow's lean Sheltie body. I look for the unspoken words behind his thick lenses.

I examine Shadow. Her temperature is elevated to 104 degrees, her heart pounds loudly as I listen, and her gums are pale. She has let slip her usual worry-eyes, and she doesn't do her usual wiggle during my exam.

"I can see Shadow is sick, but I want to run some blood tests to confirm what I suspect."

Soon the rapidly rotating machine that performs the test is silent. The small glass tube holding a few drops of Shadow's blood tells me what I fear. She is anemic, losing red blood cells faster than her body can manufacture them. Other tests confirm the cause, autoimmune hemolytic anemia. The body's immune system is on a rampage, destroying good red blood cells at an accelerated rate.

I have done battle with this condition before, but the outcome is always uncertain. The treatment is aimed at suppressing the immune system until new red blood cells can be manufactured. The cause for the immune reactions remains a mystery.

"How did Shadow get this?" the young man asks. "Will Mehan be okay?"

"Mehan will be fine." I reassure him.

One week later I re-examine Shadow. She looks thinner. Her snappy horse-trot gait is gone, and now her tail hangs limp between her back legs. I know the answer to my question, but I ask anyhow.

"How is she doing?"

"Not too well. She won't eat much, and hardly does anything but lay around. She eats snow."

I listen to her heart, and hear hollow reverberations as the heart struggles to find blood to pump. Her temperature has returned to normal, but her gums look pale and yellow.

"She has jaundice now." I try to explain the process. I read only worry in the young man's eyes.

"Her liver is overworked, trying to remove all the damaged red blood cells. The yellow gums tell me the liver is failing."

I redo the spinning blood test in the glass tube, and I discover Shadow's red cell count shrinking. I add additional medications to my treatment, hoping to halt the red cell destruction before Shadow slips away.

Shadow's owner only nods at my instructions.

"Call me if she gets worse, or if she starts breathing heavy, with her mouth open." I hope for improvement.

The next day Shadow is worse. I listen again to her heart. I hear a hollow echo and a faint rapid tic-tic-tic. Her breathing is rapid. I test her blood, more red blood cell loss. I see the yellow color intensified in her gums. Her eyes are yellow now, too.

"Can we do anything else?" asks the owner.

"I know of no other medicine. But a blood transfusion will help Shadow until she can make more of her own cells. Leave her with me, now, and you can pick her up this afternoon."

Reluctantly he hands me Shadow's leash. With his finger tips, he wipes a tear from the nose piece of his glasses. He walks out the door.

I map out in my mind the necessary steps for the transfusion. I mentally gather the supplies I need: blood collection bottle, intravenous catheter with long tubing, tourniquet, and donor dog. What about a donor dog?

On such short notice I think of only one dog, my own, Dasha. She is my big and strong Husky, from Janet's second litter. Janet called her Wilma Whiner, but I thought Dasha more appropriate.

I think about tranquilizing her, and shaving her neck for the needle. I think about her playfulness suppressed. I rebel inside. I can't do this. What if the tranquilizer harms her? What if I take too much blood and she dies? What if she doesn't like me afterwards? She won't understand. Irrational thoughts, but I must do this or Shadow will die.

I begin. Dasha resists the tranquilizer injection and whines. She looks directly into my eyes, and I can read hers. "Why are you doing this to me?"

I question the hopelessness of the situation as I drain blood from Dasha, more blood than my heart wants to take, but just what my head tells me is needed. No substitute will save Shadow – she needs every drop of dark rich blood I collect. I keep telling myself.

Dasha's warm blood fills the bottle that will bring life back to Shadow. I finish the process, and put Dasha in the kennel to recuperate.

Now, I prepare the front leg vein of Shadow for the transfusion. She doesn't resist, but lays limp on the table, breathing rapidly in-and-out, in-and-out.

I insert the catheter, and a few drops of Shadow's blood flow out onto the table. It looks like watered down Kool-aid. With so little blood, her body gets less oxygen, and the lungs and heart are working fast-as-they-can in a losing attempt to supply oxygen to every cell.

I connect the intravenous hose to the catheter, and Dasha's blood begins to enter Shadow's vein. Dasha's blood is a rich red color in contrast to the *Kool-aid* of my anemic patient.

Shadow rests her head on my lap as new blood travels through the tube drop by drop. My fingers on her chest feel the pounding heart and rapidly moving lungs as they work to keep up with life.

Gradually a transformation takes place as each drop flows from the long tube. First she lifts up her head and begins to look around. Her brown eyes thank me for what I am doing. Her tail thumps out an occasional beat as I scratch her behind the ears.

"It will be all right," I say, again and again.

Soon I notice the wildly pounding tic-tic-tic heartbeat fades into a more steady and recognizable lub-dub, lub-dub, lub-dub. Then her panting and strained breathing vanishes. Now she is restless and wants off of the table.

Finally the last drop of blood enters her vein, and I remove the catheter. I see before me a different Shadow, active and anxious to go.

I place her in the kennel adjacent to Dasha. She stares, wagging her tail at the strange collapsed dog in the next cage. Shadow can't comprehend the sacrifice given for her.

Robert Pope

Dasha weakly moves her head in response to my voice calling her name. The effects of the sedation are still at work.

I'm filled with joy and sadness both as I look at the two dogs. I begin to cry – not knowing why. I feel sadness for my Dasha, lying so still and lifeless, but also I feel joy and hope for Shadow's recovery.

It's then I realize the tears I cry are for another. For now I understand, a little, what God has given for me when He gave His Son.

98

chapter
19

C-SECTIONS

"Whatever can go wrong – does go wrong." That observation is known as Murphy's Law. Veterinary medicine doesn't escape this law, and at times seems to embrace it: for whenever animal health problems exist, things can go wrong. That's why it's called the practice of veterinary medicine.

Take the breeding of dogs for example. Just mention of this by a client and Murphy rises to the occasion, and troubles begin.

One owner wishes to breed her dog and does everything according to the book. She feeds her pampered Pomeranian the very best diet, she is patient, she counts days, she watches for the right signs – every detail is planned perfectly. After the breeding is complete, the waiting begins. Her dog looks pregnant, her dog acts pregnant, her dog seems pregnant, but after 64 days there are no puppies – a false pregnancy. No physical reason can be found, no hormonal reason can be assayed, no reason at all . . . except she wanted puppies. Murphy's law is working fine.

Another owner doesn't want puppies. His companion is a playful golden retriever, six months old to the day. An appointment has already been made to spay her, but she spots blood on surgery day – no surgery now. Spaying a dog in heat is not wise. Instructions are given to the owner to watch his dog closely so she doesn't get bred. Another appointment is made to spay her in six weeks."

Of course, that night in the dark while the owner walks his in-heat dog, the neighborhood thief of the night, Zoro, leaps from nowhere and leaves his mark. Sixty-four days later eight black puppies are born, all looking like their masked father. Another example of Murphy's law at work.

Sometimes it's worse. The small poodle bred by the large Great Dane has trouble whelping, then it's time for a C-section.

Surgery should be immune from Murphy's Law, because planning and control are practiced to perfection. But C-section surgery is different, because it's emergency surgery. Here speed supersedes planning, and control collapses during the necessary swiftness of the moment.

These are the times that test a veterinarian's skill. These are the surgeries I remember most. They can be a great joy, or a tremendous sorrow. Planning for C-section surgery is a problem, because it just happens, often at the worst time.

* * * * * * * *

I still remember my first canine C-section, a small Cock-a-Poo-type named Ginger. Gail, the owner, loved her dog. Ginger was bred accidentally and was well along in her pregnancy when I first saw her. She was puffy-bloated with water weight, a watermelon on toothpicks.

Sickness had a grip on Ginger during the last few days before delivery. She almost died from pregnancy toxemia, a condition where the basic body metabolism fails. The medicine and treatment Ginger received helped enough to allow her to roll around for a few days before D-day (delivery day).

But D-day produced trouble instead of puppies. Try as she could, bearing down, and encouraged greatly by Gail, Ginger couldn't budge her puppies. It was C-section time.

Gail was worried, because I explained that I couldn't, in all likelihood, save both the mother and her puppies. Ginger had already been through much.

"I don't care about the puppies – just save Ginger," said Gail.

"Do you want me to spay her too, if I can?" (I contemplated miffing Murphy next time).

"That would be nice."

I made plans for surgery while Joyce, my surgical assistant, prepped the patient.

After Ginger was anesthetized, I began the surgery by making a long incision. Minutes later I removed the first puppy from the open and slightly bleeding uterus.

She was lifeless.

"The anesthetic and early pregnancy toxemia must have been too much for these puppies," I said.

I dropped the lifeless body into the garbage can with a revolving lid that served as the surgical waste disposal area, and I continued to work and plop the bodies into the garbage. After the fifth and final puppy was removed, I started the process of repair by putting together what I had taken apart. I was involved in my work, careful and precise because I didn't want to loose Ginger as well.

Then I heard it. I heard a noise, a tiny squeak, directed from the garbage and muffled by blood soaked surgical gauze and other waste. I ignored it, but the noise grew louder – louder still – rising above the refuse and refusing to be ignored.

"What's that?" I asked.

Joyce shook her head from side to side in disbelief.

"Better get them out of there!" I shouted.

One by one Joyce fished for the puppies. She warmed and rubbed each one, blowing gently on them to stimulate their activity. All the puppies survived. Amazing.

Gail kept the first born – the smallest and loudest – the original garbage-pail puppy. She named her Brandy, and she still makes me laugh when I remember her first few moments of life.

* * * * * * * *

Life's first few moments are not always so happy. Chichi, the Chihuahua and her puppies are a case in point. Chichi was the pride and joy of Jane and George. This Laurel and Hardy couple were not ordinary pet owners. They lived Murphy's law moment by moment. George was the slim, timid Laurel who smiled through it all. Jane was the large round Hardy, who, in know-it-all fashion, told windy stories of all their woes including all the whys.

This couple lived in a Laurel and Hardy tragedy. On one occasion Jane related to me how their car broke down, then blew up. Their telephone worked only sometimes (when it was connected). If they had an emergency with their pets, they used a neighbor's phone, or just drove to the veterinary clinic without calling (if the car worked).

A long line of disasters followed their pets: one was stolen, another run over by a truck, a third nearly died of heat stroke in the car on the hottest day of the summer, and a fourth was kicked in the head by a horse. But through it all they remained stoic, because Chichi, the Chihuahua puppy, was going to make them rich "when she has her puppies."

I didn't see Jane and George often, but the day dawned eventually for Chichi to deliver her long awaited prize. Their phone was disconnected so they rushed to my office panic stricken. Jane presented Chichi to me in a weakened state.

103

"She's in terrible trouble. She can't have her puppies," said Jane. "Our phone is out and the car doesn't work right, and can you do something to help Chichi?"

George stuttered his concerns, smiled, and nodded his head in approval of his wife's story.

I examined Chichi carefully, and told them surgery was unavoidable.

The C-section went smoothly, and Chichi delivered four puppies. They were alive, but weak – very weak. I could detect faint movements and tiny breaths, but no cries like normal newborn puppies. After several minutes their mouths squeaked out a cry asking for nourishment which they accepted from Joyce without a struggle.

I hospitalized Chichi, who was in no condition to begin the care of her shaky brood. I sent the puppies home with instructions for care: 1) keep the puppies warm with a hot water bottle, 2) feed them every four hours, 3) clean their little bottoms with a warm wet wash towel, 4) don't use a heating pad – it will burn them.

Trouble started almost immediately. Later that night Jane called from a pay phone. She and George had been out – a short while (4-5 hours), and one puppy had crawled away from the rest. He was cold and not doing well. By morning the puppy had died.

I sent Chichi home after she regained her strength, but she proved to be a poor mother who wouldn't feed her puppies. Jane used a heating pad to keep them warm which caused burns on their feet and abdomens.

I sent home special puppy feeding formula and more instructions for proper puppy care, but one by one they died, and within three weeks the last one was gone.

No specific disease process propelled the puppies to their end. They just withered and died because they never got off to a good start. Truly the saddest C-section I had performed.

* * * * * * * *

Some C-sections are surprises, some bring sadness, and others are just astounding. I will always remember Irish Water Spaniels for that reason.

Irish water spaniels are not a common breed in the United States, once counted around 1,200. These large chocolate brown dogs have kinky curly hair everywhere except on the long, almost rat-like tail.

Their hazel colored eyes give a distinctive quizzical look to the Teddy bear face.

Ken and Peggy had been breeding Irish water spaniels for some years, and these breeders were not novices at raising puppies. Ashton was their plum, and had already delivered two healthy litters.

Peggy called one Saturday worried about Ashton's pregnant condition. She was getting progressively larger and more sluggish each day, and still there was no sign of whelping. Peggy had lost a female in labor once, so she was taking no chances with Ashton.

Ashton was not Ashton when I saw her – swollen everywhere except her head – she looked like a bloated barge ready to burst its precious load. I probed and poked and examined her carefully, looking for possible problems. She was healthy and vigorous, but just not ready to have her puppies, so I sent her home. I told Peggy to watch closely for signs of trouble, and I knew she would.

Sunday passed without word about Ashton, but Monday did not. Ken called at 3:30 in the afternoon, concerned. Ashton had not delivered – she was larger than Saturday (if that was possible) – and now she was weak, almost unable to stand.

Bring her in," I said. "We'd better operate!"

Ken willingly agreed.

Since Ken lived a good 45 minute drive from the clinic, I wasn't worried when 4:30 passed. But by 5:30 I was impatient. He finally arrived with Ashton at 5:45. Who looked more worn was hard to say. Ken had spent over an hour coaxing his 85 pound pregnant Iris Water Spaniel into their van. Ashton waddled step by slow step up a ramp he had constructed.

During the wait for Ken to arrive, Joyce and I had prepared everything for surgery. We had time to double check all the equipment and supplies, something unusual with C-sections. But prepared as we were, nothing – but – nothing could have prepared us for what was about to flow forth from Ashton's uterus.

I anesthetized Ashton and prepped her for surgery. I began the operation, making the incision, cutting carefully through several layers of tissue. I extended the length of my incision several times to allow room for the puffed up uterus I could see beneath, then I manipulated the uterus to the incision site and cut into it.

I paused for a moment – the fluttering heartbeat moment – in C-section surgery when the first puppy is removed. The puppy squirmed in my hand – then cried. I examined him carefully. He was fine – Ashton would have a healthy litter.

I exhaled, momentarily relieved, and passed the puppy to Joyce. From here on the surgery should be easy.

Joyce rubbed the puppy, gently cleaning him, and stimulating his new lungs to breathe in the air necessary for life. I squeezed the uterus and removed the next puppy – passing that one to Joyce, who performed the same rubbing procedure on the second puppy.

Then I went into the uterus for the third – fourth – fifth – sixth – seventh puppies.

"I'm not finished yet," I shouted.

I continued squeezing out more, and more. I ran out of assistants to help give puppy rub downs. I called a good friend to help with the care, but even so there were more puppies to rub than hands to do the rubbing.

Finally I dislodged the last puppy from the uterus – the one stuck in the birth canal.

I paused to gaze at a sleeping, deflated Ashton.

What a change!

She went from fat to thin like a grocery sack emptied by a group of hungry teens. The final count of squirming, screaming, crawling, puppies totaled eighteen.

Eighteen healthy puppies to be fed, and not a runt in the litter. Even with five people, feeding them was going to take time, and we couldn't take our eyes off them for a second. One nearly squirmed off the table top and landed in the garbage can . . . with a revolving lid.

The litter is now registered as a record for the breed, according to Ken who did some research.

* * * * * * * *

C-section surgery is like this. Sometimes new life is a surprise like Ginger's, sometimes weak like Chichi's, sometimes robust like Ashton's. Sometimes record breaking litters are born, other times only a few weak ones. The same surgical procedure performed each time, and yet, the outcome can be so different.

Murphy's law may prohibit planning, but it has little to do with the outcome. Success happens with nurture of the mother and preparation for the new life. That's what makes the difference.

In a way, preparing the mother is like preparing the soil for seeds to be sewn.

Another story is told, a story about the sower. He went out and sowed some seed. Some fell by the road, some fell on rocky places and places with thorns, and other seeds fell on the good soil. Some yielded a crop of a hundred fold, some sixty, and some only thirty.

ASHTON AFTER

chapter
20

CALFMAN

My day started by briefly looking over the list of stops. It would be a long day. My job consisted of inspecting calves and the facilities on several farms, then, giving special recommendations about health measures. I was a veterinarian imparting consulting wisdom, instructing and teaching those who choose to listen. In this capacity I was more in the prevention business, rather than care of sick animals. I liked the role, and the opportunity to discuss with owners the basics of good animal health husbandry things I had seen and learned in 15 years of veterinary practice that made the difference for successful farmers.

As I drove up the long winding driveway to the first farm on my list of stops, I made a mental list of my important points: proper feeding practices, good ventilation, and judicious use of veterinary drugs.

No one came from the calf barn, so I knocked on the door of a rustic country home. I was greeted by a vast man with broad-shoulders and gray white hair and beard. His attire consisted of stripped britches and stocking-bare feet. After exchanging cordial formalities, he invited me inside. I followed him down a hallway sprinkled liberally with a young child's toys. A blond-headed boy wearing a disposable diaper and half buttoned-up flannel shirt played quietly with a toy truck on the kitchen floor. I sat down at kitchen table.

"My wife, Artis, isn't here," the man said, "I'm in the baby business until she gets back."

After these brief words, he stood across the room from me and said nothing, his eyes measuring my presence before proceeding.

During this silent awkwardness I surveyed the room for clues about my host. My eyes first caught hold of several watercolors: cow-hands herding long horned steers, Indians hunting buffalo, and horses running free across the plains. The pictures told a story while decorating the walls beneath the high wood beams of the ceiling. The lived-in kitchen sprouted up empty coffee cups and baby bottles on every counter space. A large window at the end of the room permitted a grand-canyon view of the horse corral outside. Facing the window, covered by the pelt of some mammal, was his chair. Next to it within arm's reach was a telephone, pad of paper and pen – his instant office. "Who is this man?" I asked myself. "What business is he in, anyway – horse, baby, or calf?"

My thoughts were broken suddenly when my host said, "I'll put some coffee on while we wait." The way he said it, and the smile that stretched out from around his beard told me that I had just passed an inspection. He did the talking.

"Horses are my first love," he said, pointing out the window toward the horse corral. "I would breed and show them if I had the proper time, but I've been in the calf business now for 25 years. It's been good to me, but it's a funny business."

The telephone rang, and I listened to the short side of a conversation about calf milk replacer.

"I'll take care of it today, I have the sample in front of me," he said.

He returned the phone to its cradle and picked up our conversation, blending it with the telephone call he just finished.

"Yes, the calf business has been good to me. I manufacture my own calf feed. It takes protein, fat, and whey. That's about the bulk of it. Doctors say fat is bad for you, but what do they know? You should've seen that baby boy when he first came to us. Nothing to him but skin. His face was ghost-like, and his eyes all sunken in. Look at him now. Do you know what he likes? Cream. He drinks cream."

The man, this Calfman, motioned with his big hand to the boy and said, "Come here son."

The boy obediently stopped playing with his toy truck, and scaled the man's legs and settled into his cavernous lap. With the Calfman's one hand acting as a back rest, and the other surrounding the glass, the small boy drank. The tiny fingers of the boy rested on one large knuckle and guided the action. With the help of the Calfman, the boy slowly drank a glass of cream. When he finished, the boy smiled up at the Calfman. He stayed in the large lap, but made no sound.

"Artis and I have had seven foster children, but this one we'll adopt. People ask why I do it. Why? Because, I've been given a lot. I guess I'm a millionaire, that's what folks say. But seven foster children, what's that? I haven't given back as much as I've been given."

His wife returned from errands, and I followed the Calfman into the barns to inspect the calves. He continued talking as if the topic hadn't changed.

"I've learned a lot about raising healthy calves in 25 years. I've remodeled this building two times and I've almost got it right. The secret to healthy calves is good air and ten foot isles. Calves breathe from the nose – so I put good fresh warm air down the front of the barn, not from behind. After all calves are babies. That's all they are, babies."

He continued talking and instructing throughout the tour. We finished the inspection. I shook his hand and thanked him. I had contributed to the conversation no more than a few words and nods of my head.

In the truck, I paused for a moment to digest all I'd heard. I realized, then, how different my role had been from what I thought it would be.

I came for a ten minute stop on a long list of calls, and stayed for two hours. I lost time in an already busy day of inspections, but I went away with much more than when I came. I came to teach, to instruct, but instead I was taught. I was given slices of wisdom about everything from calves to babies. In short and in the words of the Calfman, "I'd been given much but I haven't given back as much as I was given."

IN MEMORY OF FRITZ ....
AND "HUMPITY DUMPITY" WHO USED
ALL NINE LIVES FAST.

21

THE HARDEST JOB

People ask me a lot of questions. But they don't often ask about the hardest part of my job. They don't ask because they know – putting pets to sleep. I never seem to get used to it, I never seem to be prepared for it, and I don't talk about it much. It's a topic nobody wants to discuss, even when the time comes. People call it "put to sleep" because it sounds good, and somehow makes them feel better than saying anything else. Veterinarians call it euthanasia because the word means good death. Pet owners just say, "It's time, will you take care of things for me?" It's all they can manage to say.

I carry out this unpleasant task again and again – still it's the hardest part of my job. I know there are no other choices, sometimes. I know it's best, sometimes. I even know it's the right time and right thing to do, sometimes. Knowing doesn't help. It's still the hardest part of my job.

It was a simple question from a five year old, "Do you have to put her to sleep?" What do I tell this child? I had not put words to my responsibility in cases of euthanasia. How can I answer this question with words for a five year old, for a grieving owner, or for myself?

I told him straight-out that God gave people the responsibility to care for animals. I told him that we must determine what's best for the animals given to our care. I told him that sometimes it's best for the animal to be put to sleep. It may not be what's best for us, but for them. I added that it was God's responsibility to decide what's best for people, because people were under His care.

He smiled back with five year old understanding – I had answered his question well. But much more, I put flesh on the skeleton of my own unspoken concerns. A hard thing to do, euthanasia, but sometimes it's best for the animal.

* * * * * * * *

"He's 20 years old and I can't care for him anymore. He's stiff in the back end. I think he has arthritis," she said. A small elderly woman tells me about her pet. The tear drops distill on the wrinkles of her face. Three almost adult grandchildren stand beside her for support. They watch in silence.

"He's been a good companion," the old woman says. Her voice cracks hoarse and strained from a mixture of age and distress. "I don't want to be without him, but I think he's suffering."

I exam the dog carefully, hoping to find a simple solvable problem. I run through my mind possible solutions as I look him over. Cataracts, gray crystallized lenses, have replaced the once sparkling clear brown eyes. His teeth – canines, incisors, and molars – are mere stubs of their former stature, and yellow-brown with age. His long black curly hair is dull and brittle, the tips streaked with white. His heart beats strong and regular (I listen intently), and his lungs are clear. But his hips joints creak out loud sounds like rusty hinges my audience can hear. I carefully manipulate each joint during my exam. They all elicit the same sound. His back legs are weak and stiff from advanced arthritis. The legs can no longer support the frame.

I scratch him behind the ears as I talk. I'm glad he doesn't hear me or understand.

"He's old and very stiff," I say. "The arthritis is advanced and causing him pain. I can't offer much help, I'm sorry."

"Put him to sleep," the old woman says. Tears now fall freely to the floor. I hand her a tissue for her eyes and nose. The decision has been made – the head knows well – but the heart rebels. She leaves the room.

The grandchildren remain, glued to the floor. They awkwardly search for something to say to fight off their tears.

"I was three when he was a puppy," says the youngest.

I inject the euthanasia solution slowly into the dog's leg vein as the grandchildren watch.

"We'll take him home and bury him," says the oldest. "It would be best that way."

The dog takes one deep breath of air, his last, and then remains still. I listen to the heart, but hear nothing.

"He's at peace," I say. "No more pain."

But these are empty, hollow words, I echo from my mouth on cue from a play I have acted out again and again. After moments of silence I help the grandchildren out the door with their grandmother's dog.

When it's quiet, I cry.

Who will be the old woman's companion now? How long will it be before her grandchildren cry at her grave?

After I dry my eyes, then, I thank God for his gift of animals. But I don't like the hard part of my job, euthanasia – good death, it is not good.

chapter
21

MAN'S BEST FRIEND

A good dog is a true companion: "man's best friend," they say. And as a true companion, he's pleased with your presence; never talks behind your back; and has endless hours to devote to your problems. Dogs demand so little: a good meal, a bowl of fresh water, a scratch behind the ear, and a walk in the woods after dinner.

My dog is a stately Siberian Husky named Tovarish (Tova for short), a Russian name that means good friend – and so he is. His eyes are coffee-brown, his ears erect and antenna-like, searching every sound, and his tail makes a bushy circle arched above his back. He carries it proud when he's in good spirits, but drops it low when he's sad. His stature is compact, and on the small side for a male, but he's a husky through and through. A good friend.

When I come home from the office, exhausted after treating an endless wave of animals and their illnesses, Tova is the first to greet me with a lick and a kiss. He often gives me that low husky howl, ar-wooo-ar-wooo-ar-wooo, that means in Husky talk, "Welcome home, where have you been?"

As a veterinarian I hear countless first hand stories of the dog who is man's best friend. For one man, his dog becomes a traveling companion, going everywhere he goes. For another, the dog is his hunting buddy, sharing the best of times. For one family, their dog is a live-in low pay baby sitter, giving hours of endless enjoyment for their three year old. For one young woman, her pet has become a serious hobby, traveling with her from one dog show to another.

A jogging exercise companion, an excuse for a long walk, a furry shoulder to cry on, a four-legged live dress-up doll, an early warning signal for visitors – countless are the ways a dog is man's best friend.

Some dogs have been good friends so long that they look like their owners, or is it the other way around? Hard to tell sometimes.

I remember Butch and his dog Mugs. Butch was stout in stature with a rough, rounded-out face and navy crew cut. An unlit stump

117

of a cigar was planted in the corner of his mouth, causing a scowl-like expression. Butch chewed his cigar, never smoked it, and talked in a low, gruff manner, but behind the rough-cut exterior was an inner mansion of character. He loved his dog.

Muggsie, his dog, was a brindle-colored, short-legged bull-dog mix. Mugs snorted his dislikes, and growled his displeasures at every visit and exam, but he rarely raised a lip to bite, and he always wagged the stub of his tail when leaving the clinic.

Butch and his companion, Mugs, made a matched set.

I have other clients that look like their pets. The tall anorectic lady who owns a Greyhound, and the lively girl with raven black hair with the ebony cat, just to mention a few.

Some owners reflect their pets in more than looks. I have clients who share the same disease as their faithful companion. One client and her dog have diabetes, another both suffer with epilepsy. One elderly lady had a bladder stone removed one month before I removed a similar stone from her look-a-like dog.

The most striking example of dog-like-owner remains in my memory as simply the old man and his dog. People in town used to say he would march his dog up and down Main street every day. The two were inseparable. As the years passed both dog and man aged together, and finally they stopped their ceremonial walks. He and his pet became confined to barracks out of necessity.

That's when I was called, one day, to treat his dog who now was well over eighteen years old. I made the visit to his home, because both the owner and his companion were too stiff to make a journey to the clinic.

I rang the doorbell several times before I detected any activity within. Then, if I listened close, I could hear the old man's slippered feet rub like sandpaper against the hardwood floor as he shuffled toward the door. He swung the door open, stabilizing his bent-over body with a wooden cane. I looked him over. His left eye appeared clouded over (probably from a cataract). This plus an opaque discharge in the corner, along with an upper eyelid that didn't function, gave the impression the eye was absent from the socket. He smiled when he saw me, exposing a toothless mouth. I spoke my name and business, but my mission fell on deaf ears. He welcomed me in after noticing my medical paraphernalia.

The dog was an aged replica of the old man. A Spanky-and-our-Gang type of dog, he was missing front teeth, limped stiffly on his legs, and had one bad eye.

I needed to put his dog to sleep. I needed to, but I was afraid to deprive the old man from his lifelong companion. Instead, I gave the dog some pills and an injection, but I held little hope for a recovery. The dog rallied from the treatment for a short time, long enough to outlast his faithful master.

When the old man died some months later, I put his dog to rest to join his master once again.

People say, "You are what you eat." In marriage the two become one. Truisms, I don't doubt. But when I see someone who has that special bond with their pet, I'm always reminded of the old man and his faithful friend who looked so much like him.

Man's best friend sometime has four legs.

THE CATS

To order additional copies of **My Patients With Tales**, please complete the information below.

Ship to: (please print)

Name_____

Address_____

_____

City, State, Zip_____

Day phone_____

___ copies of My Patients With Tales @ $11.25 each $_____

Add $3.00 shipping and handling for 1ˢᵗ book
and $1.00 for each additional copy $_____

WI residents add 5.5% sales tax (.62 each) $_____

                  Total Amount enclosed $_____

Make checks payable to: Dr. Robert W. Pope

Send to: Pause Printing
         c/o Dr. Robert W. Pope
         912 West Fourth Street
         Mosinee, WI   54455